BEYOND the SCALE

EMOTIONAL HEALING FROM FOOD ADDICTION

BEYOND *the* SCALE

EMOTIONAL HEALING FROM FOOD ADDICTION

DEBRA MOSS

Certified International Health Coach (CIHC)
International Association for Health Coaches (IAHC)

Published by Best Seller Publishing®, St. Augustine, FL
Best Seller Publishing® is a registered trademark.
Printed in the United States of America.
ISBN: 978-1-956649-35-2

For more information, please write:
Best Seller Publishing®
53 Marine Street
St. Augustine, FL 32084
or call 1 (626) 765-9750
Visit us online at: www.BestSellerPublishing.org

CONTENTS

SECTION IV:
PUTTING IT ALL TOGETHER

DISCLAIMER

The contents of this book are for general instruction only. Each person's physical, emotional, and spiritual condition is unique. The instructions in this book are not intended to replace or interrupt a reader's relationship with a physician or other professional. Please consult your doctor for matters pertaining to your specific health and diet.

This book is for educational purposes only. The views expressed are those of the author alone. The reader is responsible for their own actions. Adherence to all applicable laws and regulations, including international, federal, state, and local governing professional licensing, business practices, advertising, and all other aspects of doing business in the United States, Canada, or any other jurisdiction is the sole responsibility of the purchaser or reader. Neither the author nor the publisher assumes any responsibility or liability whatsoever on the behalf of the purchaser or reader of these materials.

DEDICATION

To all those who have been looking for approval,
you have it through the love and grace of Christ Jesus.

PRAISE FOR *BEYOND THE SCALE*

Beyond the Scale is a personal and intimate account of a journey to self-healing that tackles difficult emotional and physical issues in an inclusive way that is easy for anyone to understand. This book made me realize the importance of taking ownership of my health, both physically and emotionally, and set me on a path to become my own advocate. Debra Moss is a gentle and compassionate voice who will guide women and men alike on their own paths to physical and emotional wellness. *Beyond the Scale* is an incredible book and should be on everyone's must-read list.

— *Aldona Martin, Licensed Wildlife Rehabilitator*

This book reached deep into my soul and prompted me to look at what, initially, caused me to look at my body in a negative light. Making peace with the body God has given you is so freeing and the beginning of an incredible journey!

— *Angel Box, Licensed Cosmetologist*

After reading *Beyond the Scale*, I understand why I struggled emotionally and clung to food in the past. I'm excited to use the tools that Debra provides to change my relationship with food and exercising balance. This Certified International Health Coach gives a practical step-by-step process not only to create sustainable weight loss but to deal with the emotional components to have real balance in life.

— *Annica Brinks, Homemaker*

God has called Debra Moss to use her own life, and what she's learned, to help others in the struggle to be healthy, happy, and whole. Her words come at a deep level and with practical steps, empowering us to overcome our struggles with health issues and insecurities concerning our weight and our inner life. As a Certified International Health Coach, Debra is a gifted, grace-filled advocate for healthy living that encompasses the mind, spirit, and body. I didn't realize how much I needed this book!

— *Margaret Montreuil, Author of*
The Art of Loving God

I had the wonderful experience of having Debra as my personal health coach. She helped me to have a healthy relationship with food and bring balance into my life. Soooooooooo excited to read this book; it's like having a piece of her beside me anytime I need to feel the love and support she is so great at providing. AND it came at just the right time — it's been so hard to be good with all the stressors of this past year, it's helping me to keep making healthy choices and to stay on track and keep going on my weight-loss journey. Thanks Debra!

— *Leslie George, Happy Traveler*

Powerful, practical, and solid advice on taking back your health from someone who has actually done it!

— *Linda Moss, Executive Assistant*

What I loved best about this book is how the author eloquently weaves faith and storytelling into her explanation of a path forward to loving our bodies, finding balance, and supporting wellness. Debra's words are both inspirational and aspirational, providing readers with the tools needed to achieve our goals and encouraging us to stay the course. After reading *Beyond the Scale*, I feel both motivated to take more ownership of my relationship with food and empowered by learning the practical steps I can follow.

— Lisa Cantor, B.Sc, M.Ed, OCT, MYP Coordinator
Ontario Certified Teacher — Middle Years Programme
IB International Baccalaureate Educational System

Reading this book is like Debra is sitting right beside you, guiding you step by step through the entire process of creating a life of balance that brings health, hope, healing, and peace.

— Novalea Feltner Saligoe, IS Director of Planning,
Indiana University Health

This book reignited my desire to discover complete health and wholeness in my body in a way that fulfills God's purpose in my life.

— Ruth VanHoven, Life and Root Cause Wellness Coach

Moss seamlessly weaves her experience with truth in God's Word so that it's applicable and encouraging. She touches the heart and informs the mind. I already can think of several people I'd like to pass it along to!

— Elaine Davis Stover, Licensed Marriage and Family Therapist

This book belongs in the collection of every woman who has ever struggled with self-confidence or speaking her own truth. So many women struggle with self-image. After reading, I am ready to take back my health, and with God's help, I know I can succeed.

— Jeannie Simpson, Owner Jeannie's
Magic Touch Cleaning Service

Debra brings out the true emotions she has felt in her health journey and helps us to better understand ours. Then bringing that into God's plan for our lives is so encouraging. Excellent book for all women.

— *Ginger Uner, Healthy Lifestyle Advocate*

A must-read for anyone who wants to have a balanced life and peace with food.

— *Jennifer Espinosa, Pain Management Nurse Manager*

Debra's insight into the psychosomatic aspects of health empowers each reader to take ownership of their wellness in every aspect of their life. Her personal experiences and loving touch give all women a practical guide to navigating life's challenges, and find healing and motivation to take back our health.

— *Brenna Buckley, SPT, Physical Therapy Student, Elon University, B.S. Molecular/Cell Biology, East Carolina University*

A NOTE FROM THE AUTHOR

Every single person is unique and made in the image of God. We all have certain issues that are part of our journey. For some it's physical, some find their biggest battles in the mental arena, and for others it's in the realm of the soul. Regardless of where you are fighting your biggest battles, remember you are never alone. There are like-minded people who care and can help you fight the good fight!

Health is multifaceted. By weaving faith and health together, my clients find peace from their struggles with self-confidence, are able to speak their own truths, come to terms with their relationships with food, and find balance. They gain new strength to deepen their reliance on the Lord.

Whether you're just starting out, in the middle, or simply resuming your health journey, this book is for you. Take this foundation and build on it.

I've included some special resources for you to gain momentum on your journey. There are no quick fixes, but you can certainly start gaining momentum today. The **MOMENTUM BUILDING TOOLKIT**, my FREE gift to you for purchasing this book, includes the following:

- How to End Self-Sabotage
- Food Questionnaire
- Twelve-Minute Peace of Mind Meditation.

www.debramosshealthcoach.com/bonuses

Your solution for
faith-based
weight loss
DEBRA MOSS
HEALTH COACH · IAHC

Debra Moss

Debra Moss
Certified International Health Coach
debramosshealthcoach@outlook.com

FOREWORD

I first met Debra in the middle of the COVID-19 pandemic. It was a tough time for everyone, especially for those already suffering — those like Debra, who was struggling with chronic lower back pain. Despite the tough circumstances, I immediately detected a sense of hope and commitment in Debra that many in her situation lack. I later found out she was a Certified International Health Coach and, unlike so many other health professionals, she actually practiced what she preached.

Over the months of working with her through her back pain, she was deeply committed to healing and highly valued her body's response to activities, whether positive or negative. She used this information, along with my professional guidance, to help her body heal itself. As you will discover in the coming pages, she not only practices what she preaches, but she has also mastered it. She has discovered how to take her health back from within, without reliance on temporary external influences, such as narcotics.

Do you struggle with addiction? A lot of people have a hard time admitting it. No one is listening to your thoughts right now, and you may not be either. But it's time to be honest with yourself. A large majority of us have something in our lives that controls us: food, work, exercise, etc. Whatever it is, it controls most of what we do and how we think. That is the definition of addiction. So, be honest and answer if that sounds like you.

During this book, Debra will help you discover the full extent of your addiction and guide you through the process of owning and taking back control of your own life through faith and mindset. Changing your life can seem daunting and, at times, impossible, but Debra fearlessly describes her own journey and takes you step by step through the process.

Jaclyn Ann Polk
PT, DPT, OCS, CMTPT, CSCS
Director of Physical Therapy, Concord, NC

INTRODUCTION TO THE
TWELVE STEPS

I've written this book with you in mind. My unique personal experience combined with being a Certified International Health Coach qualifies me to share a proven formula that works for permanent weight loss.

Clients come to me with motivation, great intentions, and determination, but they lack the structure needed to bring their plans to fruition. A health coach can be an invaluable asset as you dive deeper into why you haven't been able to sustain your weight loss in the past. This is the difference between changing your patterns for a few weeks and undergoing a permanent transformation.

If you're looking for accountability from a proven, holistic weight-loss coach, then schedule a strategy session to ensure we're a good fit. Go to https://schedulewithdebramoss.as.me.

I'll take you from being stuck and frustrated to accomplishing your health and wellness goals in a sustainable and doable structure that fits your life.

I invite you to enjoy this journey as we walk together through the same proven structure I used to lose almost 100 pounds. Use the powerful, practical outline in this book as a step-by-step guide to help you live the life God has designed for you to live.

I've set this book up into three main sections: mind, soul, and body.

Mind: The first section helps you reframe how you see and use food. It gives you tools to start taking your thoughts captive.

Soul: The second section will help you understand and examine your own root cause.

Body: The third section is full of practical ways to make small changes that add up to big transformations.

I would be remiss if I didn't mention that you can't change all areas all at once; that will only lead to being further overwhelmed. You need to work through these changes one at a time. I've designed this book to take you step by step through each area. I've outlined small, simple, doable steps in each section for you to gain momentum and make lasting change. Follow along and do each step as you read that section.

I've provided room for you to write your notes in the book. Some have found it helpful to simultaneously use a separate notebook. A notebook would provide you with a place to dig deeper and write your thoughts and prayers as you dive into the foundational steps that will usher in your own transformation. It will also serve as a journal to record the victories to which the Lord has brought you in each area and the obstacles you've overcome.

This is not another "quick fix." Take your time, get comfortable, relax, and get ready for sustainable change that leads to transformations in your mind, soul, and body. Allow this book to guide you on this next leg of your journey. Prepare and expect God to meet you every step of the way as you find balance and take back your health.

Section I: MIND

STEP ONE

A TRUTHFUL EVALUATION

Honesty is the first chapter in the book of wisdom.
— *Thomas Jefferson*

I've had my struggles with health. I'm sure many of you have faced some overwhelming odds in the arena of health too. We experience pain and loss in our own individual ways. What unites us is that we are human. We never give up. We keep searching, learning, trying to find new ways to deal with setbacks, embrace life, and move forward with renewed hope.

I wrote this book because, like many of you, I've experienced health setbacks. Some ailments have simply been utter nuisances. Some defined my existence for years. Some even left me shattered, feeling as if I would never heal and never be able to fit the pieces back together again.

I've dealt with long-term pain. I'm no stranger to physical therapy and the hard work it takes to regain muscle mass. I know what it takes to make a comeback, and I also know what it feels like to be so utterly engulfed by grief that it is as if everything is moving around me at breakneck speed but I'm stuck in slow motion.

I have endured multiple surgeries. At the height of sickness, I was on fifteen medications and wore a Holter heart monitor at night, in addition to my sleep apnea machine.

I've endured bone-on-bone pain in my spine for decades because of a genetically inherited bone disc deterioration. Eventually, there was nothing left to absorb the shock of normal movement in my lumbar region where these discs were missing. I finally had an anterior and posterior spinal fusion. Following that surgery, I spent six months in intense physical therapy learning to walk again.

> *The purpose of writing this book is to assure you that no matter what you've endured, or had to wade through, no matter how fractured or shattered your life may seem, there is hope.*

I also had a vocal-cord issue that started with an episode of laryngitis resulting from the usual seasonal sinus infection. I developed dysphasia and found myself unable to make any sound, even though I desperately tried for two months to just make a single syllable or peep.

This set off a cascade of physical therapy for my vocal cords to the tune of three sessions per week for nine months. During this time, I had to use a speech app on my phone, to communicate. I typed words into my phone and a computer-generated voice would speak my message. Given the fact that I'd spent much of my life studying music, singing, being vocally trained, performing in choirs of every type, and even winning medals at a state level, this was a devastating blow. Music is simply elongated speech. I couldn't even speak, let alone sing.

I can't express how elated I was after almost a full year of this crazy routine to have my vocal cords strong enough to utter words again. Imagine not being able to tell your son goodnight or that you love him — in your own voice.

The purpose of writing this book is to assure you that no matter what you've endured or had to wade through, no matter how fractured or shattered your life may seem, there is hope. You can experience health, hope, and healing. Keep searching and pushing for answers, communicating with your healthcare provider, seeking alternative methods, and taking steps daily to improve your own health status.

Most importantly, you can learn to stand up for yourself and become your own best advocate for your health and life. You know when something is wrong, when you just feel off and things are out of balance. I encourage you to press on and fight the good fight. Surround yourself with those who will support you and cheer you on to the finish line. This is your time to rise and take back your health.

Foundations are important. As a faith-based, holistic health coach, I incorporate the Bible along with a behavior-, science-, and psychology-based approach. Every human is made up of three main elements. We are spirit beings, with a soul or consciousness, and we live in a body.

Use this book; go step by step to slowly implement what I have provided for you to start being your own best cheerleader and health advocate. It is possible. Start today. You will be glad you did!

When you build something, you need a gauge, guide, pattern, or standard. To start building a strong foundation, let's start with the Bible, the unequivocal Word of God.

> *All Scripture is inspired by God and profitable for teaching, for reproof, for correction, for training in righteousness.* (2 Timothy 3:16, American Standard Version [ASV])

God's people need to use the Bible as our standard. I'm grateful for modern medicine and the life-saving procedures that medicine, surgeries, and doctors perform every day. They save countless lives and have extended the lives of so many.

> *Jesus answered, "The foremost is, 'Hear, O Israel! The Lord our God is one Lord; and you shall love the Lord your God with all your heart, and with all your soul, and with all your mind, and with all your strength.' The second is this, 'You shall love your neighbor as yourself.' There is no other commandment greater than these."* (Mark 12:29–31, New American Standard Bible [NASB])

Let me ask you, are you loving God with all your heart, all your soul, all your mind, and all your strength? Maybe you're loving Him with all your heart, most of your soul, and trying to love Him with your mind, but what about the last part?

How strong is your body? Do you tire easily? Are you too tired to fully enjoy your life?

Are you carrying extra weight that impacts your daily life? Do your knees or back give out by one o'clock in the afternoon or earlier? Are you carrying more than the extra physical weight measured on the scale?

What about shame and guilt? Do they accompany you 24/7?

What about feelings of inadequacy? Do they relentlessly plague your thoughts?

The beauty of using the Word of God as our standard of measurement is that we can see where we stand and know exactly how our lives and hearts measure against it. At any given time, day or night, we can read a verse and ask ourselves, "Is this true concerning me?"

At that precise moment, we know right where we stand. I compare it to being at the mall and finding the map. There is a huge red X with the words YOU ARE HERE. I can't describe the incredible relief that washes over me and the comfort of knowing exactly where I am. Yes, I've been lost a time or two in a large mall — think Mall of America big. The most wonderful part is you can clearly see where you are now and identify where you want to be. There is something incredibly satisfying about seeing how to get to your destination.

The Bible is our map. If you are lost, look at the map. Our journey is marked with grace and love that perpetually encourage us to keep going and reach the goal.

Standing there, looking at the map, seeing where we truly are is like an audit of ourselves, a truthful evaluation.

You might say, "That's all well and good, but what does this have to do with the quality with which I serve and love God?"

Well, I'm glad you asked! I, too, didn't think it was a big deal until one day when my daughter was ready to learn to ride her bike *without* training wheels.

Allow me to share with you one of the most profound days in my entire existence. It shaped my journey and helped define my purpose.

My daughter was begging for the training wheels to come off her bike. She was a big girl now. She could do it! After all, it's a rite of passage for so many children to learn to ride a bike without training wheels.

The much-anticipated day finally arrived. This was the day she would ride without training wheels. I wanted this to be a monumental event, day, and rite of passage for her. I didn't want to forget anything, so I made a list. I was looking forward to this day, perhaps more than she. I wanted everything to be perfect, just like her.

I loaded my minivan with a camera — yes, I had a cell phone, but I didn't use it for photos back then — her bike, a water bottle, helmet, knee and elbow pads, a wrench to remove the training wheels, and of course, my daughter.

We headed for a nearby quiet neighborhood with gradual rolling hills. I thought to myself: Nothing could possible go wrong. I parked my minivan under the shade of a big oak tree and unloaded the contents I had so carefully and thoughtfully placed in the van.

A huge Cheshire cat smile was shining from my daughter's face. She was ready and so was I. She got busy right away, putting on her armor — helmet, knee pads, and shoulder pads — and proudly placed her water bottle in the clip on the bike frame. I took the unwanted training wheels off her shiny pink and purple bike.

She took off like lightning and didn't look back.

I tried to keep up with her. What started out as a brisk walk turned into a slow trot, and then quickly became a sprint as she approached the first of many sloping hills.

"Mama, I can't slow down!" she exclaimed with undeniable panic in her voice. I yelled for her to use the brake. "But Mama, it's not working!"

She began to shout it repeatedly, and each time was louder and filled with more terror.

As much as my heart wanted to be right beside her as she accomplished this beautiful yet petrifying rite of passage, my body could not keep up. In addition to my heart beating out of my chest and being completely out of breath, my knees ached, and a sharp pain shot down my legs, radiating from my back.

She was about 360 feet beyond my reach. That's about the length of a football field.

"Mama, help me, I'm going to crash!"

YOUR PERSONAL EVALUATION:

What things have been holding you back physically from living in the freedom that Christ wants you to have in the physical realm?

DIG DEEPER:

What one thing can you change today?

It might be how you think about yourself.

Note one way you can start to change your story today.

REPEAT AFTER ME:

I'm going to serve God with my whole mind, soul, and body.

STEP TWO

MY MOMENT OF TRUTH

If you tell the truth, it becomes a part of your past. If you lie,
it becomes a part of your future. — John Spence

Health, hope, and healing are attainable. Many things stand in the way of living how we originally intended. Fear, stress, being overwhelmed, a lack of quality sleep, a lack of fresh water, a lack of sunshine, carrying extra weight, or being severely underweight, and poor diet are just a few of the things that stand between you and your improved health.

The great news is that you have more control over these areas than you may currently be exercising.

Obesity is not a result of a lack of character, willpower, or motivation. It could be caused by a combination of hormones that may be out of balance because of your environment and stress, or by late-night snacking and decreased movement throughout the day. These factors are compounded by the standard American diet and food pyramid, amid other issues that plague our society.

I've written this book to address this unfortunate, all-too-common issue that has spiraled out of control for many people. It desperately needs to be addressed, along with the stigmatism associated with obesity. This is the real epidemic that has stolen our health, hope, healing, and happiness for far too long.

I found myself among the ranks of this ever-growing epidemic. I really wish I could say I was awakened at the very moment of my truthful self-evaluation while helping my daughter. The truth is, I felt horrible for not being able to physically keep up with her and help her on one of the most memorable days of her life thus far, as she learned to ride her bike without training wheels.

Was I completely out of breath, panting, my heart beating right out of my chest, with heavy palpitations that brought weakness to my chest and jaw, with the feeling of an elephant sitting on my chest, with every joint in my body aching, feeling like the whole world was spinning, light-headed, and, yes, let's not forget, utterly embarrassed that my body had let me down?

Yes! A resounding Yes! to every single one of those.

Was that enough to make me stop, pray, and ask God for direction, guidance, and help regarding my health or weight?

I'm ashamed to say, no. No, that wasn't my turning point.

In the months that followed, I experienced more of these same symptoms, and they consistently increased even without physical exertion, like they did during the prior event with my daughter.

I went to see multiple doctors who all seem to have attended the same university. They all had the same prescription: lose weight, exercise, and stop eating junk food, aka "empty calories." After appointments with eight different doctors, eight co-pays, and eight co-insurance payments, I still had no real answers. I was subjected to CT scans, saw a neurologist, was fitted for and wore a Holter monitor, and underwent a sleep apnea test, all of which failed miserably.

Finally, after being poked and prodded by some of the best phlebologists in the city, I heard these magic words: "We are sending you to see a rheumatologist."

What? I'd heard the word, but I wasn't sure of the scope of their practice.

The rheumatologist they recommended was in my insurance network, but appointments were fully booked out for six months.

So, another six months passed. I still felt miserable — picture the Michelin Man and you've got the general idea. I was exhausted. I never felt like I got a good night's sleep, despite using the sleep apnea machine. I felt so stuffed after eating, yet I was still ravenously hungry after every meal.

I still attended all the same church meetings, choir practices, and Bible studies as I read my Bible looking for real answers as to why I felt I was held prisoner to food.

The six months passed slowly, but the day of my rheumatology appointment finally arrived. I went to it expecting another run-of-the-mill test to be followed by yet more blood draws and the famous words: lose weight, exercise, and stop eating empty calories.

Instead, I received the most comprehensive exam of my life. It lasted four hours.

This is the day I experienced what I can only categorize as a magnitude 9.8 quake on the Richter scale of my heart.

Nothing could have prepared me for the words I heard this healthcare professional utter. After grilling me on what seemed like every detail of my entire life since age five, he turned and looked at me with the most somber eyes. In no uncertain terms, he began to tell me with dire urgency that if I did not make changes that very day, I would undoubtedly cut my life short. He was saying that if I didn't make multiple changes immediately, I might not even see my daughter graduate from high school.

He said that I would live with excessive pain, on medication that would do more harm than good, and my body would soon be rendered almost useless. He guaranteed that if I kept up this current pace, I should resign myself to a miserable existence, albeit short-lived.

I burst into tears. I'm not sure if it was because of his stern delivery, or the exceedingly long hours of endless questions that I thought had absolutely nothing to do with anything.

Or, perhaps it was the physical part of the exam and his persistence in asking me to stretch and bend like a Barbie doll as he measured my flexibility, or lack thereof.

Maybe, just maybe, it was the sincerity with which he delivered the stark news.

This is the day I experienced what I can only categorize as a magnitude 9.8 quake on the Richter scale of my heart.

I sobbed like a child. At this point, the fact that my mascara wasn't waterproof no longer mattered. I didn't care. This was a sobering realization. I was going to die within a few short years if things didn't change, if I didn't make the necessary changes and correct the long-held, deeply engrained routine behaviors I had come to find comforting.

It was in that precise moment that I awakened. It was as if I had been shaken from a long, deep stupor. He was talking to me, not my neighbor or some other person who was on a prayer list from church.

Yes, God used a rheumatologist to awaken me.

The 9.8 earthquake I suffered in my heart that day changed the course of my life forever. This was my moment of truth. This was my moment to allow God's redemptive power to transform me. I had read, studied, prayed, and believed for others, but I never honestly believed I could change my own health. At the core, I didn't think myself worthy.

I truly thought I was beyond redemption as far as my body was concerned.

The realization now standing before me was this simple question: Would I choose life, or continue in the habits that were literally killing me?

I honestly believed with all my heart I would die in this size body, never having fulfilled the call in my life as a believer in Christ. I thought my body was beyond redemption…until this moment. Then and there, my zeal was rekindled. I wanted to walk in obedience and do the things He had given me to accomplish here on the earth for His Name's sake.

I wanted to obey Him with all my heart, mind, soul, and body.

We all have moments of truth. The actions you take from that point forward are up to you. You can move forward with the help of the Lord while He's stirring your heart, or remain in the long, deep stupor, awaiting the next wave of mercy to awaken you.

YOUR MOMENT OF TRUTH:

Have you had a wake-up call?

If so, what was it?

What are you doing to act on it?

DIG DEEPER:

Are you ready to act on this, even if it's one small step?

REPEAT AFTER ME:

The things I do today are the foundation for my tomorrow.

Click here or go to https://www.debramosshealthcoach.com/bonuses to download your free guide: "How to Practice Mindful Eating."

You'll learn how to develop a healthy relationship with food by practicing healthy eating.

STEP THREE

WHY DIETS FAIL

You're only one decision away from a totally different life.
— *Debra Moss, Health Coach*

Obesity is linked to cancer, high blood pressure, type 2 diabetes, stroke, and a wide variety of other ailments.

It also plays a large role in your career. Data suggests that people who are obese miss more workdays per year than those who are not.

Obese and morbidly obese individuals have more health conditions associated with increased rates of work absenteeism, according to a study from 2007 that appeared in the *Journal of Occupational and Environmental Medicine.* It recorded a staggering $4.3 billion loss per year in the United States alone.

Here are a few of the truths we will explore about why diets fail:

- Why is sugar so addictive?
- How marketing companies lie to us.
- How a "diet mentality" is suffocating us.

God no longer dwells in buildings made of brick and mortar. One of the great and beautiful mysteries of God's love for us is that because of the price Jesus paid on the cross, God now dwells in us. We are the new tabernacle, the indwelling of the Holy Spirit.

Truth be told, this body is just a container, an "earth suit" for our inner being, our spirit being to inhabit and carry out the plans of God, the love of God, and the preaching of the Gospel while on this earth.

People often think that everyone has to eat; it's a part of life, and God loves me and understands my weakness. I'll show you how I went from thinking this same way to finally breaking free from the shame and fear, and from being controlled by food. It is possible to live free from the power of food to control you and reclaim your health, hope, and healing in the process.

The answer does not lie in the solutions the world has to offer. We've all tried those temporary solutions with either no, or very little, real sustainable outcome. You deserve to know the truth about transformation and about the single most important missing piece the world will never offer you.

This is a book about health, hope, and healing. At the risk of sounding like a broken record, obesity is not a result of a lack of character, willpower, or motivation.

It is not a lack of love for God.

> *The problem with severely restricting diets ... is that they jolt your body into "starvation mode," preventing your body from burning unwanted fat.... [When the body can no longer get its calories from food, it] looks to get some of it calories from lean muscle. This results in muscle loss. Less muscle means a slower metabolic rate—and in this case, stalled weight loss.* (Dr. Mehmet Oz, Oprah.com, "Dr. Oz Reveals the 5 Diet Myths Making You Gain Weight")

Diets don't work. Restrictive strategies set us up for failure in the long run. Please hear me — it's not your fault. Restrictive diets have a yo-yo effect. This means that if you start a severely restrictive weight-loss plan, you might drop 20 or 30 pounds, but you will gain those back, plus another 10 or 15, within a few weeks. You'll also lose lean muscle mass in the process.

We've had years of conditioning and being set up to crave the dopamine hit that sugar provides. You crave dopamine. This is a natural thing for your brain to have, and there are natural ways to get it. Processed sugar is not one of those natural ways.

The addictive cycle goes something like this: When you eat something high in sugar content, it increases dopamine levels rapidly and you get a natural high — think carbonated drinks and big fluffy snack cakes. After the initial dopamine spike starts to wear off, you go into withdrawal. Now you have to eat more of those same nutritionally devoid foods to help you feel good temporarily.

Sugar increases dopamine. The problem now becomes that the more you ingest of the carbonated drinks and fluffy snack cakes, the more you crave the natural high. The first hit of dopamine is always the strongest. Now you need increased quantities of carbonated drinks and fluffy snack cakes to get the same kind of enjoyment, the same natural high that the sugar created.

Do you see the vicious cycle that is established?

Again, it is not your fault.

The natural high or dopamine hit you get is not quite as good the second time. That is the cycle of addiction. The food industry is aware of it. It has entire teams devoted to making foods more addictive.

Yes, you read that sentence correctly!

A peer-reviewed scientific study published in August 2007 on the science site plos.org, which was conducted at the University of Bordeaux, France, by Magalie Lenoir, Fuschia Serre, Lauriane Cantin, and Serge H. Ahmed, stated that "Sugar alone was found to produce a powerful reward response, as demonstrated by a study in which rats were allowed to choose between pressing two levers: one lever gave them access to sugar-sweetened water, and the other a dose of intravenous cocaine. The rats preferred sugar over cocaine."

Let that last line sink in.

Dr. Joel Fuhrman is a board-certified family physician and six-time *New York Times* best-selling author and nutritional researcher who specializes in preventing and reversing disease. He is also the president of the Nutritional Research Foundation. He has this to say:

> *Food addiction is a chronic, compulsive overconsumption of certain types of highly palatable, low-micronutrient foods — usually high in sugar, flour, salt, and oil — despite the negative health consequences. Food addiction often involves the uncontrollable pursuit of a mood change. The addictive foods excessively stimulate the reward centers of the brain, creating an almost irresistible craving for them.*

People who suffer from food addiction find that they get a "high" when they eat their trigger foods, followed by a "low" when they are not digesting food. The condition is chronic, progressive, and — given the unhealthy nature of the addictive foods — potentially fatal. (Dr. Joel Fuhrman, Drfuhrman.com, "Food Addiction")

Again, not your fault. We are set up to crave these foods. Now, with this new understanding, if you could learn to eat and feel better, look better, have more energy, and lose weight for the long term, would you give it a try?

This time would be different from all past attempts. How do I know it will be different? That's simple: because now you know that the odds, the marketing, the media, and the food industry are all working against you, not in your favor.

This preoccupation and love affair that society has with the "diet mentality" only leads to heartache, more shame, and confusion. A quick fix is never the answer.

This preoccupation and love affair that society has with the "diet mentality" only leads to heartache, more shame, and confusion. A quick fix is never the answer.

The yo-yo effect created by dieting simply reinforces the quick-fix mentality. The bottom line is, if it sounds and looks too good to be true, then it probably is.

Just how much is the weight loss industry worth globally? Well, that's an excellent question. According to a report published on October 31, 2019, "The global weight management market was worth $189.8 billion in 2018. Weight management is the process of adopting lifestyle and dietary changes in order to maintain a healthy body weight."

Since the turn of the century, the epidemic of obesity in the United States has grown significantly worse. An article published on February 27, 2020, in *U.S. News & World Report* was headlined, "The U.S. Obesity Rate Now Tops 40%." The story reported that:

It's been two decades since federal health officials said the U.S. was experiencing a "growing obesity epidemic" that was putting millions of lives at stake — but the situation has gotten significantly worse since 1999.

At the turn of the century, 30.5% of American adults were obese, meaning they had a body mass index of 30 or higher. That rate largely increased through 2015–2016, helping to fuel related health issues like diabetes, cardiovascular disease, and some cancers — all of which are among the leading causes of death in the U.S. According to data released by the Centers for Disease Control and Prevention, the obesity rate reached 42.4% in 2017–2018 — surpassing 40% for the first time. (U.S. News & World Report, February 27, 2020)

A recent article titled "How Fat Is America? An Overview of Obesity Statistics (2021)", written for *Livin3* by Staci Gulbin, RDN, was published on March 9, 2021. It said:

This large percentage of obese Americans in statistics appears more startling when you also include the percentage of Americans who are overweight. As you can see in the chart, all together, over 70% of Americans are either overweight or obese.

The percentage of obese Americans is greater than the percentage of Americans who are overweight and is also greater than the percentage of Americans who have a normal weight.

Essentially, most Americans are overweight and it doesn't look like this will change anytime soon. ("How Fat is America?" Staci Gulbin, RDN, March 9, 2021, Livin3.com/obesity -statistics)

The chart she refers to was drawn up by the National Center for Health Statistics. It articulates the following statistics for Americans over twenty years old:

- 28.4% have a normal weight or are underweight
- 32.1% are obese
- 31.8% are overweight
- 7.7% are severely obese

There are multiple ways to measure your current health.

The Body Mass Index (BMI) is just one tool used for taking a snapshot of your current health.

Your waist-hip (or waist-to-hip) ratio (WHR) is the dimensionless ratio of the circumference of your waist to that of your hips. You take your waist measurement and divide that by your hip measurement (W÷H).

There are more tools, such as a weight scale. You can also take your overall body measurements, see how your clothes fit, and know the levels of your blood sugar, blood pressure, and cholesterol — the list goes on. All these numbers are important and together they paint a more accurate picture of your overall health.

One tool often overlooked and left out by many is the answer to this simple question: How do you feel? Are you exhausted? Do you have aches, pains, swelling, heartburn, brain fog, and chronic constipation?

There are many ways to measure our health. It's time to take a holistic approach to weight loss and not rely on the quick fix. We must look beyond the quick-fix mentality. It creates a mirage. It's truly an illusion. It won't last. Nothing worth having should ever be attained quickly.

I want to remind you that you are uniquely created. You have gifts, talents, and skills that this world needs. Your children, nieces, nephews, family, neighbors, and many others need the unique way that only you can represent Christ on this Earth.

You were created for fellowship with God. Your body was designed to serve you here on Earth as you serve Christ.

Are you the apple of your Father's eye?

Are you cherished?

Are you loved by Christ?

Emphatically, yes!

> *Blessed be the God and Father of our Lord Jesus Christ, who according to His great mercy has caused us to be born again to a living hope through the resurrection of Jesus Christ from the dead.* (1 Peter 1:3, NASB)

If you repented your sins (those knowingly and unknowingly committed), and you asked Christ into your heart, then you are born again. That fact is true. We will all see Jesus one day and give an account of our lives.

Are you living life to the fullest? Are you making the most of the price Jesus paid at the cross? Or do you identify and see yourself in the story I shared about my daughter wanting to ride her bike without training wheels?

Are you barely existing, exhausted, emotionally spent, not really present, living on the sidelines? Are you emotionally present for yourself and those in your life?

Maybe you share the same silent prayer I once did: "God, I love you with all my heart, but please let me die in my sleep to get relief from the constant pain, shame, guilt, and imprisonment from food."

The constant pain wasn't just physical. It had permeated every area of my life. Emotionally, I ran from confrontation. Much like a trash compactor, I stuffed my emotions with food. I used food to numb the pain.

Mentally, the gymnastics in my head were just too much to keep up. I was always running on empty and felt like I was at least ten miles from the next fill-up.

Physically, I had a broken body. I was exhausted all the time and yet, when I did go to bed, I never got real restful sleep. There was no restorative sleep. That's what is supposed to happen when sleep occurs: the body repairs nightly. This gives the brain a chance to defrag, much like your computer does when you shut it down for the day. I can assure you that no repairs were going on in this body, other than the minimum needed for daily functioning.

The truth is, even my rheumatologist had data to back up those facts for me.

We've discussed physical and mental exhaustion. Last, but not least, let's discuss the spiritual aspects. I prayed and believed according to 1 Peter 1:3 and I was born again, but far from free. Spiritually, I wasn't growing in Christ the way I knew I wanted to — not consistently, anyway.

Real freedom, and especially freedom around food, had eluded me my entire life. I used food much in the same way others might use alcohol or gambling. It was my comfort, and I didn't realize how much control I had relinquished to it over the years.

I had lived in deprivation in every single area of my life for so long that I didn't think twice about how I might be eating this way too. I never consciously said, "Oh, let me just deprive myself with restrictive meal plans and programs that a rabbit couldn't survive on and surely I'll feel better."

No, but if I have to be totally honest, it just seemed natural. I had been running on empty and was utterly depleted in every area of life for so long that I never stopped to question those methods.

I think somehow, deep down, I felt that because I was the one eating to soothe myself emotionally, even though I wasn't hungry, it was my fault. When I examined this area of my life, truth be told, I didn't think I deserved God's mercy, grace, or deliverance from my addictive behavior.

Have you ever eaten out of boredom, when you were overwhelmed by life, when you really should have just gone to bed because you were exhausted, or when you felt fearful, anxious, or guilty? You are not alone. I promise that you don't have to face this alone either.

There is an anonymous quote that says, "If you want something you've never had, you must be willing to do something you've never done."

This quote can be applied to every area of our lives. I used it personally and professionally as an administrative assistant for over thirty years, but never regarding my eating habits. When I applied it to my food addiction, it helped me reframe how I saw things. For the first time, I started to see that I reached for food as more than physical nourishment.

I reached for food to bring comfort and satisfaction, as a "legal numbing agent," just something to fill the void, to keep me awake when I was exhausted and trying to work. I had an epiphany: I'd been soothing myself this way for most of my life.

Most of all, I reached for food as a dear friend who was always there for me no matter what. No judgment, no harm, no foul.

The scary thing is that I'd been missing out on genuine comfort for years. I didn't know how to be present in the moment, to enjoy a smile from a friend, the sound of birds chirping, or even being content.

I realized that if I ate when I wasn't hungry, then food was not a healthy solution in that moment. I had to learn that food cannot solve my problems. I realized that I had simply been going through the motions of life but was never awake enough to engage or be emotionally present. This was a radical thought for me. Food was never intended to take the place of real comfort, or to be a cheap substitute for really dealing with emotions rather than stuffing them down deeper still, like an overfull trash compactor ready to break at the next emotional crisis.

I was going to need a factory reset!

I had to learn to have grace with myself and step out in faith to believe that I could heal from these unhealthy behaviors.

I love Psalm 34:18, New International Version (NIV): "The Lord is close to the brokenhearted and saves those who are crushed in spirit."

I definitely qualified!

All my past dieting attempts, deprivation, and this deeply ingrained hate and loathing I had for my very own body left me beyond brokenhearted and crushed. My love-hate relationship with my body for constantly letting me down was skewed on the side of hate, not love. I'm grateful for His unmerited favor, grace, and patience that He displays for us.

I'm grateful He used a rheumatologist to awaken me.

I invite you to allow God to be your comforter in all situations. Learn to be at peace with the whole beautiful range of emotions you were given by Him. Give Him ownership as your comforter and stop allowing an empty, shallow substitute to comfort you or take His place in your heart, mind, soul, or body.

Remember that we were made to crave the dopamine fix our brains need. However, there are natural and healthy ways to replace the hit the highly refined sugar gives us.

Your brain was held hostage and trained without your consent.

Think about that for a moment.

As a child, when you were sick you probably had a parent, aunt, or grandparent bring you soup, Jell-O, pudding, ice cream, sherbet, 7UP, or crackers to help comfort you and make you feel better. Part of this soothing practice may have included staying in bed, not going to school, and having more time with that special individual who brought you the food.

Basically, you got to enjoy one-on-one attention from your caregiver, who was trying to soothe you and help you feel better.

Please don't misunderstand me; I'm grateful to have had someone look after me when I was sick. The problem was not with their efforts or behavior.

The problem was that I unconsciously built a bridge, a connection in my brain that goes something like this: When I'm tired, exhausted, ill, feel inadequately equipped to emotionally respond to someone, or simply don't want to deal with a current situation, I believe I need to self-soothe with food or a special treat. The medical term for that bridge or connection is "neurological pathway." Once formed, it's a path you use over and over. In other words, this pathway gets stronger with repetition until the behavior becomes the new normal.

How do you change a self-soothing pattern that involves food or any other addiction? What would that look like?

Well, let me share a personal example of how I learned to overcome this. This is not comfortable for me to share, but I know it will bring encouragement to you as you start to identify your self-soothing patterns.

First, a little backstory. I grew up, like many of you, in a home where conflict was a natural part of life. Conflict can take the form of sibling rivalries about who will ride in the front seat of the car or whose turn it is to do the dishes. Conflict happens when more than one opinion is expressed. Now, for some of you, it was handled fairly, and you saw that everyone's opinion was valued and considered equally.

However, as a young child, I saw conflict as a bad thing, a negative thing. From my perspective, it was never going to end well, and it was never truly resolved. If you're familiar with the phrase, "Just sweep it under the rug," then you are very familiar with the emotions that follow.

When there were conflicts in my house, it always ended with voices becoming louder than they should, with doors being slammed shut, with communication being abruptly interrupted. Sometimes it led to someone getting in the car and leaving for a period of time.

This pattern continued and one day my world turned upside down when someone got in the car after a heated debate and simply didn't return.

Now, don't get me wrong. It wasn't always like this. There were some fun times, good times, fantastic family trips, unforgettable birthday parties with all my friends in attendance, times of peace and joy, smiles and giggles, and some great memories.

But the underlying tension never seemed to be resolved. It lingered and hung like a shroud over my heart.

Although I couldn't articulate my feelings, I always felt as if I was enduring the tension, just waiting for a glimpse of joy to return like a long-lost puppy or a favorite toy that had been temporarily misplaced.

Technically, conflict is a healthy part of life. If you learn how to handle it correctly, it can be a very healthy thing.

What does conflict have to do with food, or eating when you're not truly hungry, or excess weight? Well, for me, it was at the root of my food addiction.

In my early childhood, I saw conflict as a bad thing. I thought, based on experience, it was not good to share my honest opinion with others. From this point of view, it was best to keep the peace and not rock the boat. If I had a different opinion, a slightly different perspective or view about a topic — no matter how small — I learned over time to just keep it to myself.

Here's the real issue: Based on my experience as a small child, conflict leads to division, isolation, pain, and ultimately to those you love the most… leaving. In my young heart and mind, I interpreted conflict to mean division that led to pain and isolation. The meaning and new definition I assigned to conflict would ultimately dictate my entire existence.

Little did I know that this single conclusion would drive my life down a road I never intended to travel. It was certainly not a road God intended me to travel either.

Did you catch it?

The issue was the meaning I assigned to conflict. To me, conflict meant discomfort and it would ultimately lead to being alone. So, I did what any young child would do. I didn't share my thoughts or true opinions with others for fear of rejection. Instead, I would journal and write about those things, the things I should have been able to share with those I loved most. These deep-seated feelings of insecurity brought about by this hurricane of emotional upheaval talked my heart out of sharing my fears and concerns with my family.

My parents eventually got a divorce.

Irreconcilable differences.

That phrase shaped my life in more ways than I ever realized. Not only was that the end of the productive, thriving, loving, and joyous marriage and life my parents once shared, but it would also have a grip on my heart and mind for decades to follow.

The truth is that conflict can be uncomfortable. If handled correctly or properly, it can be a very healthy exchange and a healthy part of life. Through the eyes of a young child, I had learned any time there was conflict, I needed to escape.

I developed a pattern of self-soothing with food, eating out of fear that I would one day end up alone. It was not a rational truth.

Nonetheless, it carried over from my childhood, and it was calling the shots. This irrational thought I clung to went unchallenged for decades before I realized I didn't have to live this way. You don't have to continue engaging in an addictive pattern either. You can retrain your brain.

The media and society have duped you into accepting, believing, and using processed sugar to meet your need for a dopamine hit. It isn't your fault. However, the decision is yours on how soon you turn this issue over to Him. God is waiting to help you overcome the areas of life that have set you back, even if you perfected your own way of dealing with it for decades.

Simply put, diets don't work.

YOUR PERSONAL EVALUATION:

What untrue *meanings* have you assigned to situations?

DIG DEEPER:

What event(s), situation(s), or circumstance(s) from your past have helped shape how you handle stress or an uncomfortable situation?

Do you have to have a cookie or donut before your meeting with your boss? Does it give you courage?

Do you need a food pick-me-up before you tackle that stack of papers you need to sort but have been putting off for weeks? Example: For me, it was conflict.

What *meaning* did you assign to your fill-in-the-blanks story? Example: I assigned the meaning that conflict ends in isolation.

Is that a true or accurate assessment of the situation? Example: Mine was not a true assessment.

If not, what new meaning do you need to assign? Example: Conflict is a part of life and will naturally occur when honest opinions are shared.

Next time _____ happens, I will say to myself: _____.

Example: Next time _conflict_ happens, I will say to myself: _I will be okay. No one is leaving my life_.

REPEAT AFTER ME:

I am not defined by my past.

I believe what the Bible says of me in 2 Corinthians 5:17, English Standard Version (ESV): "Therefore, if anyone is in Christ, he is a new creation, the old has passed away; behold, the new has come."

STEP FOUR

TAKING EVERY THOUGHT CAPTIVE

*Sow a thought and you reap an action; sow an act and you reap a habit; sow
a habit and you reap a character; sow a character and you reap a destiny.*
— *Ralph Waldo Emerson*

Thoughts do matter. Every single thought does matter.

Ralph Waldo Emerson was giving us a recipe for a life filled with purpose. Did you catch the slow progression from one item to the next? Let's break it down further:

- Thoughts become actions
- Actions become habits
- Habits shape character
- Character creates destiny

Let me share one of the foundational Scriptures that helped me reshape my thinking:

> *We are destroying speculations and **every** lofty thing raised up against the knowledge of God, and we are taking **every thought captive** to the obedience of Christ.* (2 Corinthians 10:5, NASB 1995)

We are instructed to destroy speculations and every lofty thing raised up against the knowledge of God. How can we do that effectively if we don't read the second half of the verse? How many of us really stop and take every thought captive to the obedience of Christ, consciously and consistently?

Maybe a better question to ask is why. Why should we take every thought captive to the obedience of Christ? They're just thoughts; they can't hurt us, right?

Let me share a bit of military history with you. Don't worry. You'll see the correlation and connect the dots in just a moment.

When fighting in close combat, a bayonet comes in handy. A bayonet is a knife, sword, or spike-shaped weapon designed to fit on the end of the muzzle of a rifle, musket, or similar firearm, allowing it to be used as a spear. According to Wikipedia.org, from the 17th century to World War I, it was considered the primary weapon for infantry attacks. Today, it's considered an ancillary weapon, a weapon used for a secondary or auxiliary purpose.

What does this have to do with taking thoughts captive?

Now, imagine with me for a minute that you are on guard duty. Your country is at war. It's late in the evening and the soldier relieving you won't be there for another five hours. It's been a long day. You've served and defended your country well.

Nonetheless, you're tired and worn out from the day's fight. The enemy managed to break through your ranks and now, instead of using the rifle for a sure shot you can fire from a safe distance, you must engage the enemy in hand-to-hand combat. You have no choice. Aren't you glad you are equipped with a bayonet?

You'll need to carry out your formal training and hold the enemy hostage at knifepoint. You need to interrogate the enemy and determine if they are friend or foe. Now, instead of "enemy," insert the word "thought" into the sentence. If the thought is friendly, meaning it lines up with the Word of God, then all is well. That thought is welcome to stay.

However, if that thought is contrary to the Word of God, it is a foe.

Your training as a soldier has prepared you. You are to take it captive unto the obedience of Christ. Simply put, if our thoughts are diabolically opposed to the Word of God, they have no authority to remain. It's up to you. You have God's power and authority to take them captive unto the obedience of Christ, as according to 2 Corinthians 10:5 (quoted above).

Now think with me about how emotionally tired you might be at the end of a long workday. You swing by school to pick up your children, and then stop by the store to buy something for dinner — keep in mind you now have children in tow.

Once you get home there are last night's dishes to be done before you can even start to cook the items you just purchased. You are just trying to get in the door with groceries and make sure the kids don't leave schoolwork or backpacks in the car. You're met at the door by the family dog, which has patiently been crossing his legs for the last few hours.

You get the picture. Life is demanding.

Now, take into consideration the kind of day you've had at work and combine that with everything that has transpired in the short hour since you left work. You bring in the groceries, let the dog out, get the kids squared away, and begin cooking dinner while also cleaning last night's dishes.

Then one of your children announces that a project is due tomorrow and they need supplies.

I can testify, as a parent, that this is a very real scenario.

By the time your evening winds down, you're beyond exhausted. You've even thought about not washing your face or taking your makeup off. To be honest, at this point you will brush your teeth, but you'll skip the flossing. You're ready to crawl into bed after everyone else has been asleep for a few hours.

You notice your phone has voicemail from a call you missed earlier during your evening's commotion. You listen to it because you have an early meeting in the morning and it could be from your very demanding boss. Unfortunately, it's a message from someone in your past, long forgotten. The message was conveyed by the voice of a person whom you had intended to leave in the past, hoping to never hear from them again.

For that moment, as you listen to the message, you're temporarily transported back in time. The message catches you completely off guard. The immediate danger is in allowing old thoughts or even emotions to surface, even for a split second; if you do, you could be at risk. The risk is being swept up in your past.

Taking your thoughts captive now takes on a whole new meaning, right?

If you had been well rested, had ordered carryout, had the maid come that day — okay, let me daydream — and had been given ample notice of your child's school project, already getting all the supplies for it, then perhaps you could have quickly dismissed the voicemail message that shook you to the core, deleting it and never giving it another thought.

Let me reiterate: Thoughts do matter. Every single thought does matter. Remember the slow progression we saw in Ralph Waldo Emerson's wisdom?

> *Sow a thought and you reap an action; sow an act and you reap a habit; sow a habit and you reap a character; sow a character and you reap a destiny.* (Ralph Waldo Emerson, Quotepark.com)

Powerful, isn't it?

We, as children of God, must live by and are held to a different standard. Let me share one of my absolute most-loved Scriptures to tie this all together:

> And **do not be conformed** to this world, but be **transformed by the renewing of your mind**, so that you may prove what the will of God is, that which is good and acceptable and perfect. (Romans 12:2, NASB)

Another verse that goes along with this idea is:

> As obedient children, **do not be conformed** to the former lusts which were yours in your ignorance. (1 Peter 1:14, NASB)

Taking every thought captive to the obedience of Christ is a sobering thought in and of itself. This is something that seriously needs consideration. The thoughts we hold regarding body image, cultural pressure, self-deprivation, comparisons, and speculations need to be taken captive, with a bayonet if you will. Are they friend or foe? Are they in accordance with the Word of God?

I challenge you to reframe the way you think about yourself and your body. The legs or thighs you are repulsed by are the same legs and strong thighs that help hold up your frame and give you stability when you walk. The extra weight you carry on your middle section is the same part of your body that once carried life, and now those miracles have names. Your upper arms that have excess skin are the same arms that pulled your child from the swimming pool when they swallowed water and almost sank.

Looking at your body and all the miraculous accomplishments it performs every single day is cause for gratitude. You don't have to tell your heart to beat, your eyes to see, or your ears to hear. They work in harmony with the rest of your body to accomplish these impressive tasks.

Start here.

Start today, taking captive every thought to the obedience of Christ.

Please accept this challenge, and you will see God start to transform your thinking by the renewing of your mind according to His promise in Romans 12:2. I admonish you to allow the mind of Christ to influence all your choices and decisions.

> *Maybe a better question to ask is why. Why should we take every thought captive to the obedience of Christ? They're just thoughts; they can't hurt us, right?*

TAKE YOUR THOUGHTS CAPTIVE:

What thought continually plagues you day in, day out?
Is it how you view your body?

DIG DEEPER:

How can you look at your body with love and compassion?
Are you at peace with your body? Why or why not?
What one thought about your body can you change today?
How can you look at your body differently?

REPEAT AFTER ME:

"I will destroy speculations and every lofty thing raised up against the knowledge of God, and take every thought captive to the obedience of Christ." (2 Corinthians 10:5, NASB 1995)

Section II: SOUL

STEP FIVE

OWNERSHIP

Until you take ownership for your life, you will always be chasing happiness.
— *Sean Stephenson*

I heard a loud crash preceded by a shriek. I heard my daughter crying, but I was still too far away to see her. There was a small hill between us, and she was just on the other side. I yelled to her as I tried to catch my breath and move toward her. Everything within me willed my body to move, yet it all seemed to occur in agonizingly slow motion.

I had failed her. I couldn't keep up. In her moment of panic, she didn't remember to use the brake levers on the handlebars, unaware she could also use the pedals to stop. We had talked through these steps many times in the days leading up to this momentous occasion. She had practiced and could stop, but only when the training wheels were on her beautiful shiny pink and purple bike. When I finally reached her, she wasn't the only one with tears streaming down her face. Crying uncontrollably, she ended up with a few scrapes, but her confidence was shattered.

We all have to be responsible and take ownership for our actions regardless of the outcome. Two crucial things were missing for me to take responsibility for my actions — dominion and control. Ownership denotes dominion and control. When it came to food, these were two things I never had control over in my own body.

Not only had I failed my daughter on that remarkable day, but I'd started to see how my love-hate relationship with my own body might one day impact her and her own self-worth.

This is the same child I had prayed and pleaded with God to have — yes, lying prostrate on the floor, crying out to God in all of His mercy to grant me a child. For years this prayer was a constant daily reminder that He is God, and I am not.

As I reflect over the previous seven years, I realize they had been wrought with much sorrow. Three years before I became pregnant with my daughter, I had been pregnant with our first child. This had always been my dream. As a little girl playing make-believe, all I wanted to be when I grew up was a wife and mother.

Our first pregnancy started well, although I had violent morning sickness. I couldn't hide the pregnancy from my friends or extended family members. Everyone knew pretty early on that I was pregnant, and they were ecstatic. This was to be the first grandchild for my husband's parents, and yet another welcome and beautiful bundle of joy for my side of the family. More than that, this was my heart's biggest desire.

I was going to be a mother.

In the third month, things took a turn for the worse. I started bleeding. I literally felt the placenta rip away from my uterine lining as my husband ran one of several red lights on our drive to the emergency room.

I felt I failed this child, and I hated my body for not being a gracious host. For years, this one single action carried out involuntarily by my own body against this innocent child and my body's lack of strength defined my life. I hadn't had the privilege of understanding how my mind could be renewed by the Word of God.

Not yet. Not in this situation.

Eventually, I began to smile again, but not a genuine, heartfelt smile. It was fake.

The very thing that should have nurtured a child as it grew to full term was exactly what, I learned, I could never rely upon again: my body. I secretly hoped to one day carry a child again, but I later found out I had issues with insulin. I had a condition called polycystic ovary syndrome (PCOS). My body couldn't use the insulin it was making. This news rocked my world yet again.

This was the reason I had had trouble even conceiving in the first place, let alone carrying a child full-term. I saw multiple specialists and I hoped to get pregnant again, but it seemed those hopes were in vain.

Long-term risks of PCOS include type 2 diabetes and heart disease. Also, with PCOS, periods become irregular. It's not uncommon to have two months with no period and then hemorrhage for the next month. Because of that, skipping a period for a few months never raised any suspicions for me. This was a normal pattern in my life. During high school, I was a repeat patient in the infirmary.

Attending a college preparatory boarding school had its challenges. Mine were compounded by the time I had to be away from class to deal with my health problems. I didn't know why I was suffering excruciating lower abdominal pain that was often followed by hemorrhaging. The doctors at the infirmary had no explanation other than that maybe an ovarian cyst had burst. I consumed copious amounts of Motrin with very little relief. It was difficult to explain what I was going through physically when there was no name for my condition.

I missed a cumulative total of eight weeks of instruction my sophomore year while attending Culver Girls Academy. That's too much time away from class by anyone's standard. Friends would stop by the infirmary after their last class of the day. Some brought copies of their notes for classes we shared. Others would pass along handwritten notes from teachers with instructions on make-up work and upcoming exams.

PCOS hampered more than my classroom expectations. It hurt my status on the swim team, my choir practice, my role in an upcoming musical, my chances of winning at the state level in a music competition, and most of all, it took a toll on my self-confidence.

Thirteen years later, I was diagnosed with the syndrome. One of the things the specialist strongly urged me to do was to immediately and drastically reduce my intake of carbohydrates, which are simple sugars. This specialist even suggested I eliminate carbohydrates from my diet altogether for an extended period to allow my body to process the insulin it was already producing.

I followed his advice because of the looming threat diabetes made to my future if I didn't act quickly. When PCOS isn't corrected, one of the many risks women may incur is infertility. Since my strongest desire as a young child was to one day marry and become a mother, I was willing to do anything to remain fertile.

Four years after my initial miscarriage, after my body's epic failure, I became pregnant again. During the entire pregnancy, I lived with the fear my body would again fail yet another innocent unborn child. This pregnancy was even rougher than my first — and we know how that ended.

By the sheer grace of God, this time I gave birth nine months later to a healthy baby girl. She was such a delight! In fact, her name in Hebrew actually means "Father's delight."

Fast-forward to the training wheels incident: this was the same baby girl who was now seven years old. She wanted to experience a beautiful rite of passage by riding her bike without training wheels. I only wish my body could have been strong, healthy, and fit enough to help usher in that big accomplishment — her biggest accomplishment in her life so far, in her own eyes at least, and a boost to her self-confidence.

Being morbidly obese is no way to live. At some point, I had to take ownership of my own life, my actions, my shortcomings, and, yes, the food my hands kept reaching for and shoving down my throat.

I'd had a love-hate relationship with food since the tender age of six. Years ago, my grandmother had a conversation with my mother about my size in front of me. Keep in mind that I wasn't overweight at this point. I was, as Germans say, "thick." My grandmother told my mother, while looking at me the whole time, "You simply have to get her weight under control, you know. Being cute or pretty will not be enough. If you don't do something now, she won't have a normal life."

> *Being morbidly obese is no way to live.*

I remember thinking at the time that this was an odd thing to hear coming from my grandmother's lips. I filed it away in my emotional memory bank, hoping to never recall it again. I was incredibly naïve.

Within the week, my grandmother had taken matters into her own hands. We had a follow-up conversation a few days later. This time my mother was not present. My grandmother sat me down and explained that her reasons for putting me on a diet were all in my best interest. She had purchased special medical-grade protein drinks from the drugstore and proceeded to instruct me on the specific details.

Starting immediately, breakfast would consist of a protein shake followed by another at lunch, and my day would conclude with a regular meal of real food at dinner with my grandparents. There were to be no snacks in between meals, no candy, no soda pop, and no more ice cream. Water was the only thing I could have *without* restraint. I quickly learned that the protein drink tasted less like chalk if it was refrigerated.

This was a devastating change in routine for a six-year-old child. You may have guessed that was the beginning of my need to control things, which included myself. It planted a seed, the thought that I was not enough, that I was not acceptable, and that somehow, I must conform to the expectations of others to be loved or valued.

Years later, I realized my grandmother's methods were careless at best, but her heart had been in the right place. My highest weight as an adult, outside of pregnancy, was 260 pounds. My frame is only five-two. That put me in the morbidly obese category.

It has taken years for me to realize that I have to be responsible for my own actions and health. That kind of ownership can only come from me. It must be something I'm willing to do voluntarily. No one can force you if you aren't ready. No amount of counting calories, praying, or even "willing yourself" works. Until your eyes and, most importantly, your heart are wide open to taking ownership (the good, the bad, and everything in between), you won't make a change — not a lasting one, anyway.

Knowing what to do and actually doing it are two very different things. In my experience, you have to come to the point where you understand your real value in light of God and His plan for your life before you're truly going to take full ownership. I didn't weigh my real value as a child of God and how important I was to the Creator of the Universe. The bottom line is that the sacrifice Jesus made on the cross is enough.

You are enough, and you are loved.

Not because of anything you have done or will do in this life. Rather, because of everything Jesus did for you when He took your sins, took the keys of death and hell, then rose again on the third day, conquering sin, shame, and darkness. The same power that lives inside of you, as a believer in Jesus Christ, is the same power of resurrection that raised Him from the dead.

If He believes in you enough to die for you to restore your right standing and relationship with the Heavenly Father, then it might be time for you to believe in yourself — again, by assigning the value He has placed in you before the beginning of time.

TAKING OWNERSHIP:

How are you taking ownership for and of your body?
What would you like to see change?

DIG DEEPER:

What can you do today to make peace with your body?

REPEAT AFTER ME:

I am learning to love my body today regardless of where I am on my journey toward health. God, thank you for giving me a strong body.

STEP SIX

FEED YOUR SOUL

Thoughts are to the soul what food is to the body.
— *Steven Furtick*

What do you pant after? Is it a certain food from childhood? Let's be real. As a young child, if you came home from school after getting an A on a test, would your mother make brownies to celebrate? What if, a week later, you came home with a D on a science project? Would your mother serve condolence brownies?

The fact is, each one of us is born with a longing to be loved, comforted, cherished, and heard.

> *As the deer pants for the water brooks, so, my soul pants for You, O God.* (Psalm 42:1, NASB)

The act of spending time together in the kitchen with your mother or, perhaps, a much-loved mother figure, whether she was celebrating or comforting you, met a deep emotional need to be loved, cherished, and heard.

Love is something we see modeled for us. The love we receive and the way it's given or received from others, especially parents, is something we emulate. It is our example, whether we realize it or not. I'm not blaming our collective group of mothers for their efforts and for doing the one thing they delighted in the most — spending time with their children. Every child wants to be deeply connected to their parents.

The problem lies in the fact that, for some of us, our souls make an association between food and comfort. Remember the neurological pathways I described earlier? This goes beyond the nutrition our bodies require and food provides. This was an emotional bond for me, and it was well cemented into my thoughts. It signified comfort, calm, and a sense of well-being.

It has taken me years to understand and appreciate that the act of baking brownies, either to celebrate or to offer condolences, was an innate response from my mother. Those days hold wonderful memories and I cherish the laughter and the tears shared in that kitchen long ago.

Our hearts are made to crave love by design. The deepest love we can experience is to be fully known by God. When we crave love, our hearts are only doing what they were made to do. The problem comes in what we fill that empty void with. If we substitute food, money, or anything less than pure love, we will run the risk of replacing that God-given craving with something that is less than what He intended. The lines were blurred for me. This was probably the beginning of my addiction with food.

The kitchen held fond memories for me. In fact, one of my earliest memories as a little girl took place in that very same kitchen. I distinctly recall sitting on the counter with my yellow-and-orange corduroy peace-sign hip huggers on and my legs dangling off the edge. I was wearing my sunglasses and pretending to be a movie star sipping Coca-Cola from a plastic martini glass.

We feed our souls with a myriad of things. Sometimes, the lines are no longer clear, and this gives room to cravings that aren't healthy. Craving isn't the problem. What we fill that craving with is the critical question. The downfall is in not allowing Christ to be our all sufficiency. I simply ask: How are you feeding your soul? I used to feed my soul in many unhealthy ways. Food, especially carbohydrates, which are relatively inexpensive to mass-produce, was the biggest offender. Just think of all those empty calories in carbonated drinks and fluffy snack cakes and you've got the picture.

Those products are strategically placed at about eye level in grocery stores and your nearest convenience stores. Yep, look closely next time you're shopping. Those items are taking up prime real estate in your local markets.

What are you using to try to fill your void that only God can fill? Have you heard the expression, "Trying to put a square peg into a round hole"? Imagine a child's toy that teaches muscle memory with several plastic blocks of various shapes and their corresponding holes. Have you ever witnessed the frustration of a child who is learning to match the shapes with the correct holes? It doesn't matter how much that child wants to force a shape into the wrong hole. The fact is that it wasn't made to fit.

They're still learning. That's the point.

There is a specific shape that will only fit into its corresponding hole. Our soul is much the same way. It was made to be filled with God. We can want and even keep trying to fill the void with food, alcohol, sex outside of marriage, gambling, being a workaholic, or any other addiction known to humankind, but the truth is you must voluntarily stop trying to force the square peg into the round hole. Then, God will show you how the desire you have, the one He gave you, can only be filled by Him.

We have free will. He will not take the square peg out of your hand.

I challenge you to ask yourself what it is you are trying to "force" into the emptiness that can only be deeply satisfied by Him alone?

> *If we take the time to stop to ask Him, and earnestly wait for His answer, then we will start to experience real freedom.*

Why are you in despair, O my soul? And why are you disturbed within me? Hope in God, for I shall again praise Him, The help of my countenance and my God. (Psalm 43:5, NASB 1995)

Our souls can be in despair. It's not pleasant, but God will allow disappointments and despair to reveal our hearts unto ourselves. He already knows what's in our hearts. He often uses circumstances, even our own ill-made choices, to let us see what's really driving them. If we take the time to stop to ask Him, and earnestly wait for His answer, then we will start to experience real freedom. This is true for every single area of our lives.

> *And we know that God causes all things to work together for good to those who love God, to those who are called according to His purpose.* (Romans 8:28, NASB 1995)

Your soul was made to glorify God, and you were made with a "round" God-shaped hole. I encourage you to put down the square peg voluntarily. It would be easier than watching you, my dear sister in Christ, continue to struggle to force that square peg into a round hole. All the wishing and wanting in the world won't change the shape.

We feed our souls with so many other things. What are you prioritizing in your life? Where do you spend most of your time? What activities are you filling your soul with? What activities do you need to trim back on or step away from during this season of your life to make more room or even free up space for God?

When you live in a world filled with shame, guilt, blame, and the other usual suspects, there simply isn't room for growth. Personal growth and development don't stand a chance.

FEED YOUR SOUL:

What things are you feeding your soul in place of God?
How will you feed your soul today? Be specific.

DIG DEEPER:

Are you growing in the grace and knowledge of Christ according to the Word of God? Remember, what you give attention to in your life will grow.

2 Peter 3:18, ESV says, "But grow in the grace and knowledge of our Lord and Savior Jesus Christ. To him be the glory both now and to the day of eternity. Amen."

If the answer is yes and you are growing, what Scriptures have become pillars of strength for you?

If the answer is no, commit to it today by giving five minutes to the Lord through reading Scripture. You can start with Proverbs or the Book of Psalms and read a chapter a day.

REPEAT AFTER ME:

I can feed my soul in healthy ways that don't involve food.
I will seek God's face when I'm looking for comfort.

STEP SEVEN

EMOTIONS ARE A GIFT FROM GOD

You are braver than you believe, and stronger than you seem, and smarter than you think.
— *A. A. Milne,* Winnie the Pooh

Emotions are from God. They were intended to be used to experience life, to help us understand our need for God, and to worship Him. Remember our verse from Mark?

> *Jesus answered, "The foremost is, 'Hear, O Israel! The Lord our God is one Lord; and you shall love the Lord your God with all your heart, and with all your soul, and with all your mind, and with all your strength.' The second is this, 'You shall love your neighbor as yourself.' There is no other commandment greater than these."* (Mark 12:29–31, NASB)

Our hearts were made to express emotions. There are so many phrases in our language that denote the heart and emotions.

Dictionary.com defines "emotion" as the following:

1. an affective state of consciousness in which joy, sorrow, fear, hate, or the like, is experienced, as distinguished from cognitive and volitional states of consciousness

2. any of the feelings of joy, sorrow, fear, hate, love, etc.

3. any strong agitation of the feelings actuated by experiencing love, hate, fear, etc., and usually accompanied by certain physiological changes, as increased heartbeat or respiration, and often overt manifestation, as crying or shaking

4. an instance of this

5. something that causes such a reaction: *the powerful emotion of a great symphony*

These are just a few of the ways we can express emotion. When we use our emotions for anything other than their original purpose, we run the risk of abusing them.

Remember the example of the square peg and the round hole? This is another facet of the same principle. For years, I stuffed my emotions with food. If I had a good day, I ate. If I had a bad day, I ate. If a neighbor's second cousin twice removed had a birthday, I would eat cake in honor of them. Yes, seriously!

Remember how I shared with you my strong connection to conflict and how I would fill the "uncomfortable feeling" with food?

Emotions are good and from God. The problem was, I never learned to handle or express emotions properly. I grew accustomed to running away from all emotions — good and bad. It was my automatic habit to substitute any and all emotions with food. I'd learned and carried on the dreaded pattern of being emotionally unavailable without realizing it.

> *For the word of God is living and active and sharper than any two-edged sword, and piercing as far as the division of soul and spirit, of both joints and marrow, and able to judge the thoughts and intentions of the heart.* (Hebrews 4:12, **NASB**)

Living in constant pain is hard, really hard. I had inherited the degenerative disc disease my dad had lived with for years. Combining that with what seemed a constant barrage of disappointment coupled to unreal expectations, I quickly turned to food. At first, food was a coping mechanism to deal with the pain and disappointment in my life. However, at some point it became an addiction. I can't pinpoint with any certainty when it crossed that line, but it did.

I used food to alleviate the pressure of the "right-now pain" and to get my mind off my struggles. Somewhere along the line, I fell prey to the Devil coaxing and lulling me into a lifestyle of using food to cope with everyday struggles. I'm talking about the simple daily things.

I vividly remember the moment when I realized I was a prisoner to food, and I needed God to deliver me and help me live a life of recovery.

Food was a constant in my thoughts, my memories, my expectations, and my emotions. Eating in excess, for me, had become no different than any other temporary vice people seek as a distraction to escape reality. I say "temporary" because it became my go-to quick fix when dealing with pain, disappointment, or any other real-life letdown. Some choose illegal drugs, alcohol, sex, power, spending, and so on.

I chose food.

Any way you look at it, I wasn't using emotions for their intended purpose. Something needed to change.

Regardless of the disadvantages I was facing, I had to stop feeling sorry for myself. I had to take God at His word and *do* what His Word commanded. I had been a hearer of the Word, but not a doer. I had been deceiving myself.

I turned to these verses for help:

For God has done what the law, weakened by the flesh, could not do. By sending his own Son in the likeness of sinful flesh and for sin, he condemned sin in the flesh, in order that the righteous requirement of the law might be fulfilled in us, who walk not according to the flesh but according to the Spirit. For those who live according to the flesh set their minds on the things of the flesh, but those who live according to the Spirit set their minds on the things of the Spirit. For to set the mind on the flesh is death, but to set the mind on the Spirit is life and peace. For the mind that is set on the flesh is hostile to God, for it does not submit to God's law; indeed, it cannot. (Romans 8:3–7, ESV)

> **Any way you look at it, I wasn't using emotions for their intended purpose. Something needed to change.**

> *If the Spirit of him who raised Jesus from the dead dwells in you, he who raised Christ Jesus from the dead will also give life to your mortal bodies through his Spirit who dwells in you.* (Romans 8:11, ESV)
>
> *I can do all things through him who strengthens me.* (Philippians 4:13, ESV)

The bottom line was, God helped me face the issues that led me to those struggles. He helped me get to the root of the issue. That's what made that time different from all the previous attempts. My previous attempts had me trying to change my behavior, but I never dealt with the root of the issue that was driving the behavior.

I knew how to temporarily conform to a new diet and its rules on the outside. I'd been doing that since the tender age of six. I'd perfected it. I never once changed from the inside out.

That was the difference this time. Changes that come from the outside in are temporary. Permanent, life-altering changes only occur from the inside out.

I was the one trying to change myself. I needed God to change my heart and the way I looked at myself more than I needed another set of rules to follow regarding a new diet. That's how I was able to break free from the bondage that had for so long dictated to my mind, soul, and body. Once I identified and pulled out the root, I replaced it, filling the space with the love of God, which is greater than the void food left behind.

Don't get me wrong, it was not instant, and it did require work and retraining on my part. Once I saw the devastation this stranglehold had on my entire life, I was more than willing to put in the effort necessary to walk in my newfound freedom. I was committed and willing to do whatever it would take.

Retraining our emotions is a process. Emotions were created to help humankind experience joy, pain, pleasure, safety, and danger. Back in cavepeople times, needs were basic. You needed food, shelter, water, and warmth. When danger was imminent, cavepeople had a heightened sense of awareness to help them pay attention and ultimately survive. These emotions helped them to be on high alert because it was a matter of life and death.

Over time, humankind learned to adapt and anticipate dangerous situations. Fast-forward to today when, unless we live in remote parts of the world, wild animals like lions or bears don't roam the streets or run loose in our neighborhoods or backyards. We no longer need our brains to be on high alert 24/7. Most of us aren't living in times of great famine or feast — not to the same degree cavepeople did.

When cavepeople came across berries or a beehive, they would gorge themselves until they almost burst. They would do the same with a kill. When they hunted for survival, they really had no way of storing the food long-term. They ended up eating the meat and the much-needed fat it contained. They had no way of knowing how long it would be before they could get such calorie-dense food again.

In essence, they were intuitively storing up in their bodies. What kind of calories do fat, berries, and honey contain? Are they any different from the super-sized sugary drinks and orders of fries we all are so accustomed to eating throughout our days? No, not really.

It was either fat or sugar. Both create a temporary release of dopamine. The brain basically has three main tasks. First, it's wired to keep you safe — think survival of the fittest. Second, it's wired for pleasure — it will seek ways to make you feel good. And third, it likes to do the least amount of work possible — it likes to keep energy in reserve.

That's why our brains like repetition.

Unfortunately, not much has changed since cavepeople days with regard to the basic tasks of our brain — no disrespect to all the medical and technical advances made by modern day neuroscientists and doctors.

The main job of our brain is still to keep us safe from harm. For me, and many like me, I found solace in food. I associated safety with food.

My point is that when we relive emotions or replay situations that were not so pleasant, our brains have a hard time knowing if what we are imagining is something that has already happened in the past or is happening right now in the present. This further proves the point that our thoughts are very important.

If you dwell on negative and unproductive thoughts, it seems to stir up more of them. They seem to multiply like rabbits. The converse is true as well. If you dwell on positive and productive thoughts, they produce thoughts of gratitude and peace. Emotions are an important and necessary part of life, and they should be embraced and received as gifts from God.

Pain is a necessary and important part of life too.

In one way, pain helps us learn. For example, if you couldn't feel pain at all, then you wouldn't have the reflexes to immediately remove your hand from a hot stove. Pain is a teacher.

I realized pain would have one of two outcomes in my life. The choice was up to me. Pain would keep holding me back from being all God intended and from fulfilling my purpose. Or, if I gave that pain to God, He would redeem it and use it for good to propel me forward.

Here's where I can share some of the science-geek parts of health that I absolutely love. Everyone has a sympathetic and a parasympathetic nervous system. They have a few similarities. First, they both originate from the spinal cord. Second, they both control physiological processes in the body like digestion, circulation, respiration, urination, reproduction, and so on. That's basically where the similarities end.

They both have very specific and important jobs within the body. The sympathetic nervous system is responsible for things like raising the heart rate, dilating the pupils, inhibiting saliva production, dilating bronchia, inhibiting the digestive organs (slowing digestion), inhibiting the gallbladder, stimulating the adrenal gland to release hormones, and relaxing the urinary bladder. These things happen automatically when we face stress and danger.

On the other hand, the parasympathetic nervous system has the opposite effect. It's responsible for constricting the pupils, increasing saliva production, reducing or lowering the heart rate, stimulating the digestive organs, stimulating the pancreas (because the digestive organs are busy breaking down food), stimulating the gallbladder, and contracting the urinary bladder.

These are all things that you want to happen — as often as possible.

You guessed it! The parasympathetic nervous system is happy when you are calm and relaxed.

Let's circle back to why this is important and how it affects you. When you are calm, peaceful, resting, and happy, your parasympathetic nervous system is calling the shots. Believe it or not, this is how you should spend most of your time. Unfortunately, many in Western society live, operate, and function in the sympathetic nervous system. The ramifications are clearly reflected by our staggeringly unhealthy rate of disease.

There are things you can do to help cue your body and stay in the parasympathetic nervous system longer. You can train your body to do them. As an international health coach, I have a few examples my clients found helpful.

One of the best things you can do, starting right now, is to take your thoughts captive to the obedience of Christ. Remember "Step 4: Taking Every Thought Captive"? If you rehash bad memories, your mind and body can't tell whether those things are happening now or in the past. It signals your mind and body to immediately go into the sympathetic nervous system — that's the fight or flight mode, which you don't want!

Another natural way to bring calm into your day and signal your parasympathetic nervous system is through your breathing. There are many simple deep-breathing techniques or exercises you can find with the help of your computer's search engine. If you want a simple technique that has stood the test of time, try this one:

1. Be seated
2. Inhale deeply, breathing in through your nose for a count of three
3. Then hold your breath for a count of three
4. Exhale completely, steadily blowing your breath out through your mouth, like you would blow out the candles on a birthday cake, for a count of six

Again, if you are new to controlled breathing, please do it sitting down. Until you become accustomed to this technique, it's imperative that you don't do it standing up, so you don't lose your balance.

You could try doing three sets either in the morning while still in bed, or in the evening when back in bed and ready to sleep. Pick one time per day and be consistent. Many clients have found this simple practice to be helpful to slow down and really pay attention to their breathing.

You can concentrate on feeling your chest rise and then feeling the chest cavity fall when you exhale. For some, this is a practice they incorporate into their daily routines. Once you've done this technique faithfully for a full two weeks, consider doing it twice a day. Remember, do this in a seated position until you are accustomed to it.

As a reminder, you can use the twelve-minute Peace of Mind meditation I created for you. It's listed at the beginning of the book as a free gift on the Note from the Author page.

Another successful method of engaging the parasympathetic nervous system is as simple as taking a five- or ten-minute walk every day. Prayer and meditation also accomplish this same state of calm. There have been numerous scientific studies that show that definitive relaxation occurs during prayer and meditation.

Stretching is an effective technique. If it's been a while since P.E. class, you might want to watch a video first to refresh your memory on correct posture and position. Some of my clients have used yoga stretches to bring their bodies into the parasympathetic nervous system.

Also: taking a warm bubble bath, playing with your pet, reading Scripture or a wonderful book, laughing — the list is as endless as your imagination.

All of these are free and easy to fit into your daily routine. When practiced consistently, they will help you spend more time in your parasympathetic nervous system.

EMBRACE YOUR EMOTIONS:

How can you begin right now to replace the nervous anticipation of emotions with the peace of God in your life?

Which technique from the list above are you going to start with this week?

Start with just one, and when you've been consistent for at least two weeks, add a second and so forth.

DIG DEEPER:

What emotions do you avoid?
How do you deal with emotions?
How can you change the way you deal with emotions as a gift from God?

REPEAT AFTER ME:

I will learn to embrace emotions as a gift from God and refuse to be driven by them.

Click here or go to https://www.debramosshealthcoach.com/bonuses for the link to get your free guide: "Physical Hunger."

It will help you determine if you're turning to food to soothe your emotions and help you build new habits with ease.

STEP EIGHT

FOLLOWING THE SPIRIT OF GOD

When you take time with God and listen to His voice,
He renews your strength and enables you to handle life.
— *Joyce Meyer*

Do any of you know a little something about being a people pleaser? I do!

Fear of rejection will drive you to override your own voice. It will make you say yes when you really need and want to say no. It is responsible for making you over-commit and take on more than you should.

The real problem is that resentment builds up when you don't speak your truth, and it will keep you in a victim mentality. Are you going to listen to your heart and push back the fear of rejection, or will you cave and end up giving all your reserves of emotional, mental, and physical strength to others?

Do you say what you think others expect to hear? Do you keep the peace, hold your tongue, and walk on eggshells just to appease the sleeping giant of rejection? If you answered yes to any of these, don't despair.

You can learn how to stop ignoring your heart, your true voice, and your gut instincts, and stop allowing your soul to be sucked dry by being a people pleaser. The biggest danger is not over-committing and becoming exhausted, although that is certainly a dangerous place to reside. No, the biggest danger is that you begin to second-guess yourself and no longer trust your own voice or gut instincts. Being a people pleaser eats away at the deep connection you have with your own instincts. If left unchecked, it will sever those ties completely.

There comes a time when you must learn how to stand up for what you believe. In this case, you need to believe in yourself.

In the past, if someone asked me to do something, I would automatically say yes, thinking I really could do it all. It created so much unnecessary stress in my life.

Lesson learned.

I remember the first few times I said no to requests that I had previously said yes to without a second thought. It was hard. It was really hard.

When I faced objections, I would end up backing down and saying, "Well okay, I'll do it." With practice and consistency, that short phase was followed by a time when I could deliver a firm: "No. I already have an appointment that day. I'm sorry. I really wish I could help."

That phase was not as hard as the first. I was getting better at saying no when I really needed to say no. My confidence as an individual was growing. I began writing appointments on my calendar — appointments to pray, catch up on sleep, go for a walk, whatever I knew I *needed* — from that day forward.

I also got much better about not "spilling the beans" about the confidentiality of those appointments. It was none of anyone else's business what I was doing at any date and time. Oh, believe me, the people who had grown accustomed to me saying yes all the time would repeatedly ask me why I couldn't be there for them.

These appointments in my calendar were not for the usual doctors, dentists, or annual mammograms. No, they were appointments I scheduled with myself.

It was a start, and I was thrilled with the progress. I had finally broken free from being driven by the emotions of fear or rejection. Over time, it became easier, and some of the worst offenders simply stopped asking.

The takeaway is that if you don't draw a line, people, especially well-meaning people, will suck you dry.

Think of it as a bank account. If you have a budget, you need to stick to it, right? What happens if you start piling up overdraft fees? The bank is not going to extend grace or credit.

Your time is on a budget too. You only have so much time here on this earth. What are you doing with the time you have? Are you going to spend it doing things that are not part of God's plan for your life? Or are you going to say no to the things that don't fit with God's plan for your life?

We all have a choice.

Let me leave you with this thought: Every time you say yes to someone else's request that is not part of what you should really be doing, you are going to be saying no to God because you've already allocated your time. Are you going to be doing all God has called you to do, or will you allow your time to be squandered?

This Scripture helped me finally stop being a people pleaser:

> *For we are his workmanship, created in Christ Jesus for good works, which God prepared beforehand, that we should walk in them.* (Ephesians 2:10, ESV)

I pray that you find the strength to stop pleasing other people, listen to your own heart-gut-instinct, and believe in yourself. God has plans that only you can fulfill here on this earth.

Make yourself fully available to the work God prepared for you.

I think John C. Maxwell, a top leadership professional, summed it up when he said, "Your calling is when your purpose becomes bigger than you."

> *God has plans that only you can fulfill here on this earth. Make yourself fully available to the work God prepared for you.*

Progressing from being a people pleaser to having confidence in your own decisions is a huge mile marker. When you stop second-guessing yourself, you will make room to hear the Spirit of God more clearly and more often.

> *For all who are being led by the Spirit of God, these are sons of God.* (Romans 8:14, NASB 1995)

Once I had moved past being a people pleaser, the next thing to overcome was my own flesh.

I had read in 1 Corinthians 9:24–27, NIV, "Do you not know that in a race all the runners run, but only one receives the prize? So, run that you may obtain it. Every athlete exercises self-control in all things. They do it to receive a perishable wreath, but we an imperishable. So, I do not run aimlessly; I do not box as one beating the air. But I discipline my body and keep it under control, lest after preaching to others I myself should be disqualified."

Being led by my own flesh and desires was something I was very familiar with. Actually, I had spent a lifetime being led by my own wants and desires. Most people start their days eating something sensible like coffee, eggs, or maybe cereal, but my days all began the same — with a full 2-liter Coke.

Yes, you read that correctly!

I knew how to be led by my flesh; I'd perfected it. I knew nothing, however, about being led by the Spirit of God. I had to learn. That meant having a childlike faith and starting at the beginning.

Similarly, infants don't start out by walking or running. They have to learn how to crawl first. It's a process that takes time. They build up their muscles and their confidence.

It's the same when you learn to walk by the Spirit of God.

I began searching for Scriptures like Romans 8:14. I wanted to be led by God and not my own earthly and fleshly desires. I'd proven over and again that left to my own devices, I would fall short of being led by the Spirit of God. I had to turn to God. I had to learn to trust Him. I began reading Scriptures that told me I could know His voice.

I started praying about small things. I remember one time in Indiana when it had been snowing heavily and it was time for my weekly grocery run. I felt silly about praying to ask God which grocery store He wanted me to shop in that day. Nonetheless, I prayed. I felt a small nudge in my heart and followed that prompting. To my amazement, the road to the store I had felt nudged toward had already been plowed. Did I mention how deep the snow was?

List in hand, I began shopping for the week ahead and I found that every single thing on my list was on sale. Mind you, I had not looked at the circular to scope out sales. This may not seem like a big deal to you, but let me assure you it was monumental for me. It gave me the confidence that I could indeed hear from Him. I was building my faith muscles.

As the weeks and months began to unfold, I continued to seek His wisdom and longed to hear His voice. The desire to please Him and spend more time in His presence grew exponentially.

A note of caution here: I was asking about things that were not of consequence to others. These were small things that affected only me. I did not start out with actions that have taken seasoned ministers years to build their faith to perform, like laying hands on the sick and praying for people to be raised from their sickbeds. I asked small, seemingly insignificant questions about which choices He wanted me to make in my life.

I wanted His input, His approval, His voice to lead me. Hearing His voice on the small things gave me confidence.

Again, small choices.

Early in my faith journey, my pastor's wife, Angel, taught a message to the women's group about the practicality of prayer. It made a profound difference in my walk with the Lord and is something I never forgot. One example she gave concerned something as small as praying about the order in which He wanted us to do our household chores. Sure, we had all developed our own patterns over the years and had our own methods of setting about our cleaning routines, but remember, I was in spiritual training. I needed to know I really could hear His voice.

Angel encouraged us to take the time to ask God in what order He wanted us to do our cleaning routines. The astounding and beautiful thing is that I found I could get more done in shorter time when I listened and acted on that small little voice, that nudge from the Lord in response to my prayer. It always amazed me how quickly I got the house cleaned. His way left me with extra time. I used that time wisely to read more Scriptures and pray. I was growing and building muscle in this faith walk. Indeed, I was learning to follow the Spirit of God.

My excitement was growing.

Wherever you are on your journey in life, you too can learn to hear His voice. Again, start with the small things, and over the months and years that follow, your confidence in hearing and following His voice will grow.

My sheep hear My voice, and I know them, and they follow Me.
(John 10:27, NASB 1995)

Therefore, I urge you, brethren, by the mercies of God, to present your bodies a living and holy sacrifice, acceptable to God, which is your spiritual service of worship. (Romans 12:1, NASB 1995)

FOLLOWING THE SPIRIT OF GOD:

Are you a people pleaser?

Do you have trouble saying no when you need to?

Do you listen to your own instincts and then follow through?

How do you already follow the Spirit of God?

How can you increase your hearing of His voice?

DIG DEEPER:

There are practical ways you can start depending on God.

I invite you to develop your spiritual muscles and walk in the Spirit in a great way today.

REPEAT AFTER ME:

John 10:27 is true concerning me.

I hear and follow the Lord's voice (John 10:27, NASB 1995):

"My sheep hear My voice, and I know them, and they follow Me."

Section III:
BODY

STEP NINE

PROPER SLEEP

Sleep is an investment in the energy you need to be effective tomorrow.
— *Tom Roth*

What if you could wake up every morning feeling refreshed, focused, and excited about the day ahead?

One key foundation for maintaining optimal health is getting adequate amounts of quality sleep. Sleep deprivation will take a heavy toll on your overall health and wellness.

Some negative effects of sleep deprivation include increased risk of chronic disease, weight gain, increased risk of accidents and injury, a decline in cognitive function, and increased anxiety. If you are feeling run-down, irritable for no specific reason, struggling to focus, or experiencing "brain fog," the culprit could be poor sleep and poor sleep hygiene.

Don't despair! There are some simple habits that will get you sleeping well again in no time.

Let's review a few facts about sleep to get you back on track. These seven points were referenced from a recent Harvard study on sleep hygiene.

First, how much sleep should you get? Find your age group in the following chart.

According to the National Sleep Foundation, in the article titled "How Much Sleep Do We Really Need?" by Eric Suni and Dr. Abhinav Singh:

- Newborns (0–3 months old) need 4–17 hours,
- Infants (4–11 months) 12–15 hours,
- Toddlers (1–2 years) 11–14 hours,
- Preschoolers (3–5) 10–13 hours,
- School-age children (6–13) 9–11 hours,
- Teenagers (14–17) 8–10 hours,
- Young adults (18–25) 7–9 hours,
- Adults (26–64) 7–9 hours, and
- Older adults (65+) 7–8 hours.

Second, you will sleep better if the room is cooler. Simply turn the thermostat down a bit before bed.

Third, remove ambient light to have the room as dark as possible. You may need to invest in blackout curtains.

Fourth, shut down all electronics at least one hour before bed. The list of the biggest electronic offenders includes TV, Facebook, Twitter, Instagram, and Pinterest. Resist the temptation of checking random emails one last time before bed.

Fifth, you might want to install an app called f.lux on your electronic devices to help reset your natural circadian rhythm.

Sixth, try incorporating light stretches or develop a yoga stretching routine one hour before bed.

Seventh, put electronics on airplane mode and, if possible, don't have them charging next to your bed.

In *The Sleep Revolution*, Arianna Huffington explains the history, nature, and science around sleep. She shares her own personal struggle and how she now fervently protects her sleep time. She describes how her sleep cycle and the importance of it has come full circle in her life.

> *I would rush through my day and then, almost as an afterthought or as just another thing to check off my to-do list, I would fall into bed.*

Having a good routine for sleep hygiene is imperative if you want to live a life that will leave a legacy. My personal sleep hygiene was deplorable. I would rush through my day and then almost as an afterthought, or as just another thing to check off my to-do list, I would fall into bed. I never gave attention to things like the temperature of the room, whether it was dark enough, or if my body was overtaxed and needed extra sleep.

I look back now and see that I was squandering the precious gift of sleep in my own life. You may not consider sleep a gift, or as something you need to prepare for, but believe me, sleep really is crucial to how well you perform everyday tasks, and how well your memory works. Your muscle reflexes, coordination, and a multitude of other important things that you need in your daily existence are improved by sleep.

The Bible is very specific about rest. The Bible shows us that on the seventh day of creation, God rested. This is a beautiful example that we should follow too. Rest is a crucial part of our lives. We need time to rest, reflect, and recharge our batteries, so to speak. However, we have all acted at one time or another as if we have an unlimited source of energy. I have done this more times than I can recall.

The truth is, we all have twenty-four hours each day to get things done.

After much soul-searching, I realized I was not Wonder Woman and I needed to stop acting like it. The reality was, I wasn't managing my time well. There were things I said I wanted to accomplish and goals I had set, but when it came right down to it, they weren't getting done.

The problem was the *discrepancy* between my intentions and my actions. Once I started to make decisions based on the things I truly felt were important, I was able to start letting go of the things that consumed my time.

If you realize you need more sleep, then going to bed earlier is one simple way to accomplish this goal. It won't happen by wishing alone. You have to plan to go to bed earlier. If this is your goal, I suggest you start by using increments of fifteen minutes. Once you have successfully accomplished this new goal, then add another fifteen minutes to this new habit until you reach the total allotment of time you had determined you needed to add.

This will mean turning off the TV sooner, turning off your phone earlier in the evening, and perhaps flossing and brushing your teeth fifteen minutes sooner than normal to help get you into a new routine. Use a timer if you need a reminder until it becomes a habit.

Another great way to gear down for bed earlier is to prepare for the next day: make your lunch, lay out your clothes, or gather your papers together so they'll be ready. This will dramatically decrease the amount of time you spend tossing and turning in bed, worrying if you have everything you need for the morning.

Any of the external cues you give to your brain and body will help you, in the long run, to make gearing down for bed a smoother transition.

> *Thus, the heavens and the earth were finished, and all the host of them. And on the seventh day God finished his work that he had done, and he rested on the seventh day from all his work that he had done. So, God blessed the seventh day and made it holy, because on it God rested from all his work that he had done in creation.* (Genesis 2:1–3, ESV)

Once you start to clean up your sleep hygiene, you'll see how much deeper you sleep and experience the benefits of more restful sleep. Believe me, you will become very protective of this precious gift called sleep.

PROPER SLEEP:

Into what age category do you fall, according to the National Sleep Foundation's study?

Are you currently getting the recommended amount?

Which one of the strategies listed above are you going to start with to get better sleep?

When will you start this new strategy?

DIG DEEPER:

Keep a journal for one full week and record how many hours you get per night. If you have a smart watch, you can change your settings to show you how much sleep you get nightly.

Record your data for one full week:

Day 1: I slept _____ hours. Tonight, I choose to go to bed at _____ p.m.

Day 2: I slept _____ hours. Tonight, I choose to go to bed at _____ p.m.

Day 3: I slept _____ hours. Tonight, I choose to go to bed at _____ p.m.

Day 4: I slept _____ hours. Tonight, I choose to go to bed at _____ p.m.

Day 5: I slept _____ hours. Tonight, I choose to go to bed at _____ p.m.

Day 6: I slept _____ hours. Tonight, I choose to go to bed at _____ p.m.

Day 7: I slept _____ hours. Tonight, I choose to go to bed at _____ p.m.

Repeat this sleep journal weekly until you are getting the right amount of sleep you need.

REPEAT AFTER ME:

I will love my body by giving it the proper amount of sleep I need nightly.

STEP TEN

HYDRATION

Pure water is the world's first and foremost medicine.
— *Slovakian proverb*

Water. What's the big deal?

Water has been essential from the beginning of time. About 70% of the Earth is covered with water.

What is the relationship between water and the human body? If I recall my fifth-grade science, our bodies are also made up of approximately 70% water. Is that a coincidence, just an odd fact, a random statistic?

No, I think it is paralleled by design.

Have you ever stopped to consider what water does for you? At the most basic level, water is responsible for carrying nutrients to all cells in the body. It also carries oxygen to the brain. These are two incredibly important functions.

I want to think clearly, and water helps me do that. If you are diligent about taking supplements, but not about drinking enough water, then check this out. Without water, the body can't absorb and assimilate minerals, vitamins, amino acids, glucose, and other substances. In other words, you're not getting all that you're supposed to get from those supplements. That's a big waste of time and money.

Another basic function of water is to remove toxins and waste from your body. Our bodies rely on the liver to literally pick up toxins from our bloodstream. They get converted into water-soluble substances that get removed through urine. Our liver and kidneys need to be supported to do their job. One huge way we can do this is by staying hydrated and helping the liver and kidneys function the way they were intended. Think of them as your friendly garbage collectors. If you're not getting adequate water, it would be like your trash cans overflowing but you never take them to the curb for pick up or removal. The color of your urine can hold some clues, too.

> *Even low levels of dehydration can cause headaches, lethargy, and constipation.*

Ever wonder what urine color says about your health? Curious about which of the ten colors is closest to yours? Check out this link to Urology Associates of Denver to find out.

Without enough water, you could become dehydrated. According to an article from December 2017 in *Medical News Today*, dehydration occurs when more water and fluids leave the body than enter it. Even low levels of dehydration can cause headaches, lethargy, and constipation.

The article goes on to state that water is found in every cell, within blood vessels, and between cells. If you thought water wasn't a big deal, then think again.

There is a delicate balance between the amount of water we need and the amount we actually get.

I invite you to participate in this simple quiz.

Take note of how many 8-ounce glasses of water you consume daily. Do you get one, three, five, or maybe as many as six in a day?

Have you ever noticed the correlation between how you *feel* when you are well hydrated versus when you are dehydrated? When you are dehydrated, do you feel tired or sluggish? Is it hard to concentrate? Are you constipated? Do you crave sweets?

Start making a conscious decision to become aware of how water, or the lack of it, affects your body, mind, and mood. It all starts with awareness and being intentional.

Your body does so many amazing things for you all day, every day. Now is your chance to do something *big* for your body!

Still not convinced? Take a look at this information from the Mayo Clinic.

Every cell, tissue, and organ in your body needs water to work properly. For example, water:

- Gets rid of wastes through urination, perspiration, and bowel movements,
- Keeps your temperature normal,
- Lubricates and cushions joints, and
- Protects sensitive tissues.

The U.S. National Academies of Science, Engineering, and Medicine have determined that an adequate daily fluid intake is:

- About 15.5 cups (3.7 liters) of fluids a day for men
- About 11.5 cups (2.7 liters) of fluids a day for women

Recommendations like these cover fluids from water, other beverages, and food. About 20% of daily fluid intake usually comes from food and the rest from drinks according to the Mayo Clinic (https://www.mayoclinic.org/ healthy-lifestyle/nutrition-and-healthy-eating/in-depth/ water/art-20044256).

Be sure to include fruits and vegetables on a daily basis to keep you hydrated. Yes, fresh fruits and vegetables add up where hydration is concerned. Great examples are watermelon and spinach, which are almost 100% water. [not sure what 100% water by weight means].

Mom was right! Eat your veggies.

HYDRATION:

The average adult needs between eight to ten 8-ounce glasses of fluid per day, depending on your activity level.
How many 8-ounce glasses do you consume daily?
Do you drink more water during the week or on the weekend?

DIG DEEPER:

If you drink an excess of coffee or carbonated drinks, then I have a challenge for you. Replace one carbonated drink, tea, or coffee per day with eight ounces of water.

Do this every day for one full week. Then increase the water by one more glass per day for another week until you have reached eight to ten 8-ounce glasses per day.

It won't happen overnight, but it can happen one day at a time. It will create a compound effect, just like interest on a savings account. Be consistent and you'll hit the right amount of water your body needs.

In case you weren't aware, caffeine is a stimulant. It's also a diuretic. It can cause you to lose more fluids.

Did you know that excess sugar can inhibit the body from absorbing water? Yikes! Think about that for a minute. Did you realize that excess sugar could do that to your body?

In the United States, coffee, soda, and tea are the most common sources of caffeine. Caffeine can also be synthetically produced and added to some medicine, food, and beverages, and is even found in some supplements.

Day 1: I consumed _____ caffeinated drinks, tea, or coffee. Today, I choose to reduce my intake by _____.

Day 2: I consumed _____ caffeinated drinks, tea, or coffee. Today, I choose to reduce my intake by _____.

Day 3: I consumed _____ caffeinated drinks, tea, or coffee. Today, I choose to reduce my intake by _____.

Day 4: I consumed _____ caffeinated drinks, tea, or coffee. Today, I choose to reduce my intake by _____.

Day 5: I consumed _____ caffeinated drinks, tea, or coffee. Today, I choose to reduce my intake by _____.

Day 6: I consumed _____ caffeinated drinks, tea, or coffee. Today, I choose to reduce my intake by _____.

Day 7: I consumed _____ caffeinated drinks, tea, or coffee. Today, I choose to reduce my intake by _____.

Take note of how you feel when you are well hydrated. Is it easier to remember where you left your keys? Are you able to recall things easier than before? You might be surprised how this very simple change will improve your mood too!

P.S. Don't worry! The extra trips to the bathroom are just an indicator that your body is removing toxins. Rejoice that something so simple as clean drinking water can have such a profound and healthy effect on your body!

REPEAT AFTER ME:

I'm showing my body love by giving it the water needed to carry out the God-given tasks and functions it was created for in the first place.

STEP ELEVEN

NOURISH YOUR BODY

The doctor of the future will no longer treat the human frame with drugs, but rather will cure and prevent disease with nutrition.
— *Thomas Edison*

Food is synonymous with nourishment, but that's only partially true. We also nourish our mind, soul, and body. We've been doing it for years. We just don't categorize things like education, learning, entertainment, favorite television series, exercise, or movement as nourishment.

This seems like a great place to share the deepest philosophy of Hippocrates, the famous Greek physician. In the year 440 BC, he said, "Let food be thy medicine and medicine be thy food." He was absolutely correct. Food in its raw and natural state has many healing properties. Science is just now catching up to prove this fact.

If food is an addiction for you, then the thing that has caused your pain could be the very thing God can use to free you. This fact is not for the faint of heart. I know the first time God began to show me that He would use the very thing that previously had imprisoned me to free me, I was speechless. Trust me, my family would testify that doesn't happen often.

Let's consider the term "satiation." According to Dictionary.com, it is defined as "the state produced by having had a specific need, such as hunger or thirst, fulfilled."

As part of my training to become a Certified International Health Coach, I learned about primary and secondary foods. Joshua Rosenthal, founder and director of the Institute for Integrative Nutrition, divides the two. Until hearing his lectures, I had never given much thought to the concept. Basically, you're getting mental, emotional, and spiritual nourishment from different areas of your life, and it's feeding you in other ways.

Wellness comprises more than what you physically eat. Rosenthal outlines the basic concept that physical food is secondary. According to Rosenthal, primary foods are categorized or grouped into the following:

- Spirituality
- Creativity
- Finances
- Career
- Education
- Health
- Physical Education
- Home Cooking
- Home Environment
- Relationship
- Social Life
- Joy

One area or category starts to flow over to another and overlap at times. Wellness goes deeper than what you had for dinner last night.

Are you satiated from other things in life besides food?

Yes.

We can derive great satisfaction in our relationships, by sewing new curtains, or by meeting an income goal. We get pleasure from a job well done, completing an education goal or project, or getting great lab results at our latest visit to a medical practitioner. What about beating our best time on the treadmill, following a recipe to cook an amazing meal, having a clean and tidy home? The love we share with a spouse or a loved one, having a few great loyal friends, and celebrating the joy of life or a newborn baby all qualify.

If I asked you, I'm sure you could come up with a long list of things you get satisfaction or meaning from doing. These are all things we enjoy, accomplishments we can share with those most important in our lives. Do you see how these can all be sources of secondary food? All these things feed us on one level or another. We are constantly feeding our mind, soul, and body.

> *Balance is a key part of our human existence.*

At the most basic level, nutrition itself involves carbohydrates, lipids (fats), protein, vitamins, minerals, and, yes, water. If you look solely to food, believing it has the capacity to satisfy all the other needs in your life, you will soon see the flaw in this way of thinking. It would be as skewed as thinking that if you are married, all you need is your spouse, as if they will meet all your other needs.

We know that is not true. We also know that is not a healthy way to think either. There is no balance in that kind of relationship. It isn't realistic to begin with and will lead to more unbalance in your life.

Balance is a key part of our human existence. Think of the seesaw, a teeter-totter on the playground. It has a single pivot point usually located in the center of the board. When one side goes up, the other goes down. If you live with one side of the seesaw completely weighed down, it will become very difficult to achieve balance between the two sides. However, if you live with some weight or pressure on both sides at the same time, it will be much easier to see when things outweigh each other and start to become out of balance. It is much easier to correct a slight imbalance immediately than waiting until things are disproportionate. If we apply this seesaw example to our lives, we can see which areas are out of balance. We need balance in our lives in order to be fulfilled, satisfied, and healthy physically, emotionally, mentally, and spiritually.

When you get married, you don't lose your identity. If you were a great seamstress or musician before getting married, then you are still a great seamstress or musician after getting married. In other words, you're adding to your existing identity and expanding it.

In much the same way, all the other categories or areas of your life should be enhanced when you add food into the mix. Food is not the sole source of nourishment, just as being a spouse is not your sole identity after marriage.

We need to know we are valued and heard. We need to know our life makes a difference in the grand scheme of things.

Here are just a few ways you can nourish yourself:

- Pray
- Practice good posture
- Write a letter to yourself listing all your positive attributes
- Take your dog for a walk
- Read a motivational book like the one you're currently enjoying
- Write down a list of things that make you smile
- Send a card to a friend
- Practice gratitude
- Meditate (HINT: Use the twelve-minute meditation from your Momentum Building Toolkit.)
- Nourish your brain — eat a handful of walnuts
- Eat a meal with as many colors of the rainbow as possible (try combining orange carrots, white cauliflower, purple cabbage, and snow peas for a stir-fry filled with phytonutrients)
- Take a bubble bath
- Record your food in a food diary (HINT: Use the one at the end of this section.)
- Text a quick word of encouragement to an old friend
- Pay for the car behind you at the drive-through
- Smile, and with genuine interest ask the cashier at the check-out line how their day is going

Dictionary.com defines the word "nourish" as "to sustain with food or nutriment; supply with what is necessary for life, health, and growth."

Make a commitment to yourself that you will love yourself with what you consume. Listening to uplifting music as you clean the house, replacing one sugary snack with a piece of fresh fruit, or reading a chapter a day of a good book are all examples of nourishing yourself by consuming something that will add to your life in a positive way.

Do you feel lousy or depressed after listening to the nightly news? If so, realize there is a connection between what you are consuming and how you feel.

Are you filling your time with activities that nourish and build you up, or do they deplete or deflate you? Are you doing things you enjoy? If not, then why not?

You have contributions that only you can make to this world. Some of the ways we contribute are by using the talents and skills God endowed upon us. One way could be by contributing to a financial project at work, or by picking up your neighbors' children at the school car line, or by giving yourself to prayer when the Spirit of God prompts you, or simply by baking a second loaf of bread for the widow next door.

We may not always see the impacts we make in other people's lives this side of heaven. We have no way of realizing the full domino effect we create when we follow our hearts and use the gifts God gave us.

You are the only one who can represent you. If you have a passion for helping others and want to crochet blankets for cancer survivors, then do it! You would be making a difference in the lives of every single person who receives one of those special prayer blankets.

There are individuals who are impacting our nation on a local and global level by using their gifts and talents for God. There are world changers all around us. Just look in the mirror and you'll see one staring right back at you.

Are you a gifted musician? Hone your skills and begin at home by ushering in the presence of God and sing unto the Lord. Write and record those songs for others to experience God's power and presence.

We all have a chance to impact eternity, and it starts right here on Earth. Reconnect to your passions and use the gifts God has given you. They will grow and multiply as you use them. God will cause the increase. That's one of His many blessings that He bestows to those who use what they've been given. It's a Biblical principle.

Is there a passion you had long ago that you've let slip or have simply forgotten? Get connected again and you will soon find your desire for food begin to wane as you find fulfillment and nourishment in other areas of your life. This is the principle of primary foods in action.

When I was a little girl, I would lose track of time when playing with friends. I was so emotionally present and connected with them in those moments that dinner was the last thing on my mind. If it was true for me, then I know it's true for you too. You can get lost or caught up in those other things that once held your attention. For example, if you enjoyed writing poetry, then get a great journal you can use specifically for writing poems.

I encourage you to explore the categories listed above and reconnect with passion. You'll find a greater sense of accomplishment, purpose, and satisfaction. I know from personal experience, you will certainly find more joy, happiness, and balance too.

How do you feel about home cooking? Do you enjoy cooking, learning new recipes, experimenting in the kitchen to make combinations that soon become your new favorites? If yes, then by all means carry on! If not, I really encourage you to try one new recipe a week.

It doesn't have to be complicated or include crazy expensive items you only use for that one recipe, or be boring. If you can boil water and make pasta, make scrambled eggs, or cut up veggies, then you are qualified. There are simple, quick, easy, and healthier versions of just about every single comfort food known to humankind.

I encourage you to start slowly and increase your kitchen skills one recipe at a time. You will have greater control over what you are eating. You'll also have a deeper connection and appreciation for the food and where it comes from.

One big emotional benefit is the satisfaction of making a dish that tastes fantastic. Who knows? You might find being creative in the kitchen sparks the creative streak you've been missing.

NOURISH YOUR BODY:

Do you eat to nourish your body? If not, why not?

Do you have a desire to start eating for nourishment? Or are you expecting food to fill all the other voids in your life?

Today, I will nourish myself with food by _____.

Today, I will nourish myself with thoughts by _____.

Today, I will nourish myself with movement and exercise by _____.

DIG DEEPER:

In the same way that you started to replace empty carbonated calories with water in Step 10: Hydration, you can do the same with food. Look for patterns.

When are you consuming most of those empty calories? Are you by yourself or with others when you consume them?

What emotions come up if you eat when you are not even hungry?

Is there a healthier way to direct your emotions?

REPEAT AFTER ME:

I commit to eat when I'm physically hungry and stop when I'm full.

Click here or go to https://www.debramosshealthcoach.com/bonuses to download your free guide, "Food Diary."

Keeping a food diary will help you become aware of your patterns and how you respond to your environment and stress.

STEP TWELVE

MOVE DOESN'T HAVE TO BE
A FOUR-LETTER WORD

*Movement is a medicine for creating change in a person's
physical, emotional, and mental states.*
— *Carol Welch*

Always being picked last for dodgeball or any other sport in P.E. class was just the way of my life. I didn't like P.E. class, the uniform, the locker room, or any other part of it.

I was not what I would call an enthusiastically physically active child. As a young child I did ballet, tap and jazz dance, and baton twirling. I was on a bowling league and would occasionally grab a basketball and shoot hoops in my driveway. Those were all forms of movement I enjoyed. I could also never get enough of riding my bike, playing with my Hula-Hoop, or swimming.

Let me tell you about my bike. I loved my bike. It was complete with a banana seat and many long, pretty tassels hanging from the handlebars. I liked the freedom a bike gave me. I didn't have to wait for a friend's mother to pick me up, or for my mom or sister to drive me to a friend's house. I could get there on my own. I loved the state of being physically unrestricted. My bike afforded me that freedom.

Eventually, I got an upgrade from that little bike I loved so much. As I recall, my favorite bike of all time became a Schwinn Collegiate Ladies 5-Speed Road Cruiser Red Breeze Racer.

Daily during that summer, I took my tennis racket along with my can of Dunlop or Wilson tennis balls and rode like the wind to the neighborhood high school. If the tennis courts were full, I'd practice my backhand on the side of the building. I would practice until dark. I couldn't get enough.

This was during the height of Martina Navratilova and Chris Evert's Wimbledon Championships. Everyone in the country was admiring the incredible tennis athletes who had made it to the top. I even bought a book with my own money so I could learn the official rules, and I stole away to practice anytime I could.

Another favorite activity was doing the Hula-Hoop. It was something I could do by myself or with friends. I recall many occasions when we would have a contest to see who could keep the Hula-Hoop swinging the longest.

One of my favorite things to do after dinner was to take our plug-in radio outside into the backyard near the pool and I would Hula-Hoop until nightfall. I never once thought of it as exercise. It fell into the category of sheer fun. I liked to challenge myself and see how many songs I could get through before the Hula-Hoop would drop. My personal record was seven.

My true passion was swimming. It was the only kind of exercise or movement that ever made me genuinely happy right to my core. I felt free in the water. I felt at home. It was my happy place.

As a child, I remember my father had severe pain in his lower back for years. He always came home for lunch. He ate quickly and then he would spend the rest of his lunch break on the living room floor, stretching out his back to try to find some semblance of relief.

He had seen our town chiropractor for years, but the relief he gave was temporary at best because of the degenerative discs in my father's back. The doctor had told him the best way to get a more permanent form of relief was to swim and use hydro jets to help relieve muscle tension.

He and my mother fit the definition of the word "entrepreneurs" long before I'd ever heard of the term. Getting our backyard pool built was a long and tedious process, but after my father drew up the blueprints for the design, he obtained permits, and construction finally began with him borrowing the Bobcat from the foundry he co-owned.

Before that, I used to swim at Forest Park. I dreamed about having a pool in my own backyard. Thanks to my dad, it became a reality. That was just the beginning. There were countless BBQs, birthday pool parties, pizza pool parties, and neighborhood friends hanging out at our pool. You name it, and we found an occasion to celebrate.

Did I mention how much I loved that pool? I still hold fond memories that were made possible by that pool. My aunts, uncles, and cousins would come over for family dinners and cookouts. Swimming afterward was just a given! I cherished our times together.

However, it was more than that. That pool was special. The time it took to draw up the plans, dig the ground, pour the foundation, create the decking around the outside of the pool, and fill the pool with water represented something more than happy memories. It was a reflection of my parents' time.

Time equaled love.

That pool was a symbol of their love for my siblings and me. It was something tangible and I loved it at first because my parents loved it. At some point, I grew to love it on my own. My parents would jokingly call me the Fish, or sometimes the Frog.

I honestly couldn't get enough time in that pool. I remember when I was obsessed with perfecting my dive. I jumped so high on the diving board that when I entered the water, I scraped the bottom of the deepest point. I still have the scar between my first and second fingers on my right hand as a beautiful memento of those precious times. I still smile when I notice it on my hand!

> *Make movement a three-letter word again. Make movement fun!*

It's hard to think about the pool without thinking of the house. My parents added to it and more than doubled its original size. That house still holds great memories for me, even though it had to be sold in the divorce. It represented love and security.

I'm happy to report, that house has been well maintained. I got a Christmas card this year from the current owners. They are still enjoying all the solid additions and upgrades my parents made over the years we lived there.

Okay, you're right — move is a four-letter word.

Make movement a three-letter word again. Make movement fun. I dare you!

Is movement fun for you? Do you enjoy moving your body or do you think of exercise as a chore? Is there a form of movement that you still love, even if it's been a while since you did it? Do you have one you really enjoy? Is it an individual sport or a group sport?

What about when you were younger? Is there something you could pick up again from your youth?

The possibilities are endless. You can start small and gain endurance and mobility. Regardless of your current physical condition and shape, you can start today by incorporating more movement into your life.

If you drive to the store and normally park close to the front of the store, try parking five spaces farther away. Make it a game and you'll look forward to it every time.

If you walk to the mailbox to get your mail every day, then increase your movement by walking there and back twice a day.

What you do doesn't have to be huge to make a real difference. Don't be fooled into thinking you have to go from the couch to a marathon in the same month.

I challenge you to reconnect with something that sparked your interest when you were younger. Do you love the idea of yoga and stretching for flexibility? Try chair yoga until you build more stability and strength, then you can do it from a standing position.

You'd be surprised what might ignite a creative idea regarding incorporating more movement into your day.

We were made to move. Did you know that sitting is the new smoking? Sitting all day is hard on your body. We were made to move. Sitting could have such a detrimental impact that it is now considered by many to be the new smoking. There are many health-related problems linked and associated with prolonged sitting.

Here are just a few:

- Type 2 diabetes
- Heart disease
- Impaired memory function
- Varicose veins
- Metabolic syndrome

When adding up how much time you spend sitting, consider the time in the car during your commute to and from work, the time you are at work, the time you sit at a table eating meals, and the time you may spend trying to unwind at the end of the day by watching TV or going to a movie. And let's not forget the computer work you may be taking home.

It really does add up!

So, what's the solution? Add in small changes throughout your day. For example, set a timer on your phone to get up from the couch or your desk and stretch every hour if possible, or maybe every hour and a half. If at work, walk to the water fountain, restroom, or even go to the stairwell and walk up one flight of stairs and then take the elevator back down to your floor.

Start small.

Put on a comfy pair of tennis shoes and walk ten to fifteen minutes during your lunch break. Your body will thank you. It's a great way to incorporate movement and clear your head. You will be amazed by the results.

Don't forget to add a buddy or a pal. Every activity is instantly more fun when you have accountability and someone to be there for you.

Walking just fifteen minutes a day could be a game changer for your cardiovascular health. If it's bad weather, you could walk in place in the living room. If your buddy can't make your usual walking time, just set a time later in the day to talk on the phone while you walk in place in the comfort of your own home. You'll still get the support that both of you need and *deserve*.

You don't need expensive equipment. In most cases, a sturdy pair of tennis shoes, a bottle of water, and a watch or timer is all you need.

MOVEMENT:

Notice, I did not say exercise.

How do you feel about movement?

What form of movement are you going to start with today?

DIG DEEPER:

How can you start incorporating more moving into your daily routine? Be specific. List what you are going to do and when.

Some examples include:

- Parking your car farther away from the front of the grocery store
- Taking the stairs for one flight to build up your endurance, rather than taking the elevator
- Standing up in between commercials
- Walking in place when watching your favorite TV show

REPEAT AFTER ME:

I commit to moving my body today.

Section IV:
PUTTING IT
ALL TOGETHER

THE MISSING PIECE

You can eat healthy food, drink good, pure, fresh water, incorporate movement into your daily routine, get great restorative sleep, and still not be truly happy or healthy.

Your thoughts and the internal dialogues you have day in, day out, are just as vital to your health as what you eat.

Do you have peace in your life, or are you a bundle of nerves, ridden with anxiety, fraught with fear, and just trying to get through the day? If so, I know that kind of life all too well. It wasn't until I turned to God for help with my weight issue that I found true peace.

Look, I didn't change everything overnight. I started with small manageable steps like those I've outlined here in this book. They added up quickly. The momentum I built made it easier to keep going. They say momentum gets you started, but commitment keeps you going.

I began to evaluate the underlying causes of my way of eating and my way of handling emotions. I examined my thoughts and patterns.

I had to be honest about my moment of truth and take ownership of the good, the bad, and the ugly things in my life. I realized that emotions were a good thing and truly a gift from God. I learned how to use them effectively while also learning to listen to my own instincts. Then I learned to follow the Spirit of God. After I had explored all those areas of my life, I learned about the role that sleep played in my life. I began to understand that my body really was the Temple of the Holy Spirit.

I was astonished to learn how important water was to my overall health. Having clean, fresh drinking water is just as important to my physical health as drinking from the Word of God was to my spiritual health. I soon learned to replace the negativity I had toward my own body with good wholesome thoughts and with the things God said about me, according to the Word of God.

I had been on every diet under the sun. If there was a quick fix, I found it and tried it. Some of them I tried repeatedly while on my journey of seeking the real explanation for the excess weight my body was so accustomed to carrying. I had prayed and read Scriptures to find the elusive missing piece. I thought I had exhausted every means possible.

That's when it hit me.

I had never actually invited God to be part of this journey in which food was involved. I had never asked His opinion on the subject.

No more was I trying to hide how much food I was consuming. You know, I was writing in my food journal or log so it would look neat and tidy, but I was not being honest about how much I ate. It was easy to write down the number of veggies or fruit servings. It was an entirely other thing to be brutally honest about how many Triscuits, cookies, Twinkies, or pieces of pie I consumed.

As if God hadn't seen me hastily and secretly eating a third piece of pie before anyone came home! Somehow, I thought by not recording that I had eaten a second or third slice, I would make it not so. Who was I kidding? I had an addiction.

Until I was ready to be honest with myself, I wasn't ready to invite God into this area of my life.

After reading this far, you may be ready. If so, that's great. However, you may not be, and that's okay. Keep reading and keep being honest with yourself. This is all preparing you for when that moment comes. Realize you are not alone.

It wasn't until I was ready to honestly ask Him to show me the root of my issue that I felt hope. I began to act on His leading and promptings. This was my path to freedom. I finally had the strength to start unpacking my emotional baggage.

The fat that I had so carefully and meticulously added, layer by layer, was no longer serving me. I no longer needed it as a chasm separating myself from people. I no longer needed a buffer between myself and others.

Until then, I had never saw how or why I was really using my weight to keep me at a safe distance from others. I used it like personal armor to prevent getting emotionally hurt again.

People are only human. They will, at some point, disappoint or even hurt you emotionally, either unknowingly or intentionally. There is no number of physical layers or padding that could ever stop that from happening. That's just a part of life.

For me, something had changed on the inside.

I no longer wanted to be invisible. I no longer had a desire to be a wallflower. I wanted to live and really experience life. I'd had enough of merely existing. I had a newfound strength and hope to sustain me.

This time it was different, and it changed absolutely everything. I somehow believed that He would take away the one secret source of comfort I had taken pleasure in and found solace in for all these years. The bottom line is, up until this point, I did not trust Him with this area of my life.

Until that time, I kept putting bandages, quick-fix diets, on my perpetually festering wound. The real root of the issue, the blistering wound, needed to be lanced so it could heal properly.

Oh, how I wish I had realized sooner that He truly cared about every area of my life. He wanted me to be free from the addiction and power that food had over my heart and mind. I had assigned value and meanings to words that were not accurate, and I needed His love and grace to show me what those were.

Until then, I had never seen how or why I was really using my weight to keep me at a safe distance from others where I could get hurt emotionally again.

I shut my heart off to Him for years out of fear and misunderstanding. It was not until I asked God to come into the most secret, hurtful, darkest part of my life that I experienced true freedom. He has been faithful to walk with me on this part of my journey too. I labored for years under false assumptions. He was not waiting for me to slip up, or to catch me, scold me, or shame me. He was on my side.

He is on your side.

Believe me, He wants you free in this area of your life, for many reasons. One reason is that if food is consuming you and taking up all your waking moments, then it leaves precious little time for the other endeavors you were placed on Earth to fulfill.

But the biggest and most important reason is that Christ died so you might be free in every area of life. That, my friend, includes this area of food and addiction.

I ask you, are you consuming food, or is it consuming you?

LIVING IN BALANCE

Living in balance means learning how to flow with the seasons of your life. It doesn't mean all or nothing.

I used to think finding a true balance between mental, emotional, spiritual, and physical health was just out of reach. I had a worldly mentality that it was all or nothing. For example, if I had every intention of having a "good food day" that meant no slipups. When I made a misstep, I'd abandon ship and say something like, "Well, I've messed up, so I'll eat without restraint and start over tomorrow."

Or my go-to was, "I'll wait for next Monday!" If I had a dime for every time I said this, I'd be an independently wealthy woman!

What on Earth was so magical about Monday? Nothing! It was my excuse to procrastinate and put off the hard work of dealing with why I was eating out of control in the first place. By saying, "I'll start again on Monday," I was pushing off ownership and avoiding looking deep inside at what was broken and justifying my behavior. I honestly believed the issue was too big — even for God. That's what addiction does. It keeps you in despair.

Figuratively, it was the mountain I knew I must climb, but I never thought I would reach the top to see the summit. I was living in direct contrast to my heart's desire to be healthy. Living at odds with myself was yet another source of self-perpetuating stress.

The great news is, there is a way to live in balance without giving up on your dreams and ambitions so you can truly live each day to the fullest. Here's the bad news that you've known all along: You must give up a few things that no longer serve you, to live in balance.

First, you have to give up an all-or-nothing mentality. It will rob you of your God-given capacity to accomplish all He has planned for your life. It will keep you in bondage to a "someday." It will keep you tethered to the idea that "It works for everyone else but will never work for me."

Second, you must abandon the idea of perfection. Let me reassure you right now: There are none perfect, except Christ, and He has already fulfilled the Law. So, no need to apply for that position.

This idea of perfection is your mind's way of trying to control life and the situations in it to keep you safe. In case you haven't heard it lately, let me tell you that you are safe. You don't need to protect yourself or keep yourself safe from ever being hurt again.

> *Nothing will change until you step off the merry-go-round.*

Then shall your light break forth like the dawn, and your healing shall spring up speedily; your righteousness shall go before you; the glory of the Lord shall be your rear guard. (Isaiah 58:8, ESV)

Third, you must create room in your life for God. If you are running from sunup to sundown and stuffing every waking moment with everyone and everything besides God, then you have a problem that can only be remedied by giving Him room. I know life can get so busy it's like you meet yourself coming and going. You find it hard to even have time to sit at the table for a meal, and you eat on the run. Nothing will change until you step off the merry-go-round.

I invite you to create margin in your life. Make it a priority.

What is "margin"?

Margin is having room in your life for unexpected things as they occur, time to read that bedtime story, time to get across town for that meeting, time to not be pressed to the last minute on a work deadline, and time for God.

We all have twenty-four hours in a day. What you do with them and how you choose to fill them is up to you. If you are always running late and are always pressed for time, you might need to add margin in your life. Take this simple quiz to find out.

The following statements are grouped into three categories of Mind, Soul, and Body. Rate your level of satisfaction for each statement. On this scale, 1 means "I strongly disagree" and 5 means "I strongly agree".

Strongly Disagree   Strongly Agree

1	2	3	4	5

MIND: MENTAL HEALTH, MENTAL STRENGTH, OVERALL MENTAL HEALTH

I have a reserve of mental strength. _____

I am never swallowed up or overwhelmed by negative thoughts. _____

I never find myself reliving conversations or imagining how I might have answered differently. _____

My mind is not often anxious or fearful. _____

I bathe my mind daily with Scriptures. _____

Record your total for this category here: _____.
This is your individual score for this area.

SOUL: EMOTIONAL HEALTH, EMOTIONAL STRENGTH, OVERALL EMOTIONAL HEALTH

I have a reserve of emotional strength. _____

I am in control of my emotions, and they glorify God. _____

I walk in peace daily. _____

I make quality time daily for prayer or meditation. _____

I don't live in the past or carry around mental or emotional baggage from days or years gone by. _____

> Record your total for this category here: _____.
> This is your individual score for this area.

BODY: PHYSICAL HEALTH, ACTIVITY LEVEL, OVERALL PHYSICAL HEALTH

I have a reserve of physical strength. _____

I don't have physical ailments that nag at me all day long. _____

I never end each day in utter exhaustion. _____

I am doing all God has called me to do. _____

I make time daily for movement. _____

> Record your total for this category here: _____.
> This is your individual score for this area.

> Add all three totals for each category here _____.
> This is your overall score.

If your total score was 70 or more, congratulations on living a life in balance and harmony! You have struck a wonderful balance. Keep making the steps outlined in this book your daily priorities.

If your score was 45 or less, you are doing some important things that facilitate margin, bring balance, and help usher peace into your everyday life. Look back at the individual category with the lowest score and start with that area first when making adjustments.

If you scored 37 or less, you need to make some adjustments now, and you'll immediately find more margin, balance, and peace in your life, starting today.

Look at your lowest score and refer to the relevant sections of this book to get started implementing changes and making adjustments to usher in more balance.

LEARNING TO LOVE YOURSELF

There are many ways you can show compassion to others. If you love someone, you're going to make sure they get whatever they need to be successful, right?

You are no exception to this rule.

If you don't make time to cook and eat home-cooked meals, keep a tidy home, take care of your relationships, make time for creativity, look after your personal or professional development, keep a good eye on the pulse of your financial health, incorporate prayer, read the Word, and spend time with God daily, you will come up empty.

You are too important to neglect.

I used to think that making time for self-care was, well, selfish.

For example, my earliest recollection of flying was when my dad took our whole family up in his Cessna shortly after he'd earned his license. I've had the privilege of flying many times since then. Some of those times included family vacations, business trips, and mission trips. I also once had to catch a red-eye in the hope of reaching my dad before it was too late, as he was lying on his deathbed.

I've heard the warnings and cautions the flight crew makes countless times. Yes, I'm one of those people who take the trifold pamphlet out of the seat pocket in front of me and follow along as they instruct the passengers on safety precautions. However, it wasn't until I was recently on a plane and heard the flight attendant recite her pre-takeoff spiel that something finally clicked.

I'm the only one who can perform self-care.

Okay, let that sink in for a moment. No one else can do this for you.

Back to the plane and the pre-takeoff spiel....

In case it's been a while since your last flight, let me remind you of the speech they give prior to takeoff.

Oxygen and air pressure are always being monitored.

In the event of a decompression, an oxygen mask will automatically appear in front of you.

To start the flow of oxygen, pull the mask toward you. Place it firmly over your nose and mouth, secure the elastic band behind your head, and breathe normally.

Although the bag does not inflate, oxygen is flowing to the mask.

If you are traveling with a child or someone who requires assistance, secure your mask first, and then assist the other person.

Keep your mask on until a uniformed crew member advises you to remove it.

Now, if you've ever flown on a plane or seen it portrayed in a movie, I'm sure you can visualize a flight attendant demonstrating that message.

I used to spend so much time and energy doing things that really didn't matter in the long run. I'll share some of my examples, so you won't feel alone if you have some too.

First example: I used to spend time folding towels and washcloths all in the same direction. On rare occasions, I let someone help with the washing and folding of towels, but if they folded a towel and put it in the closet in the "wrong" direction, I would literally stop what I was doing, unfold it, and then refold it the "right" way.

Sounds silly, right?

Well, do you remember all those earlier references to perfectionism? Yep! Okay, moving on.

Second example: I have a weekly pill organizer for my vitamins and medications. In the event that I've forgotten to take all my supplements for the day, I will rearrange them so that section for that day is empty. It bothers me to see some left over. It's similar to making a to-do list and writing down things you forgot to add to the list but you've already spent energy on...so, you write them on the list just to cross them off. Am I the only one who will admit to this?

Alright, before you diagnose me as having OCD, think about some of the things you spend energy and time on that really don't matter. I bet you could list them right now. I'm talking about things that are not life and death, but you treat them like they are.

For example, I arranged those towels as if an inspector were going to pay me a surprise visit. Really, who cares how they are folded? I have a cabinet door that closes and conceals them. Do you see how easily energy can be used up on things that shouldn't require that level of detail?

My point is, those towels were not worth the amount of time and energy I was pouring into them. I would have been better off using that time to establish and practice a self-care routine.

Self-care is not limited to things like getting a massage. It's much more. It's about realizing there is just one *you* and it's time your name appears on your long to-do lists.

I've heard it said that you'd be a better (insert your station in life here) when you become well rested and have the bandwidth to take care of others. I believe that to be true. I've lived both ways, and I can attest that being relaxed, well nourished, having enough sleep, and being "prayed up" is the better version of me. I'm sure my family would wholeheartedly concur.

Here is my challenge to you:

- Start now by writing *three* things you are grateful for today,
- Put *fifteen* minutes in your calendar to do *nothing*,
- Have an *extra* glass of water,
- Go to bed *earlier*, and
- Have an extra serving of *vegetables*.

It's not complicated. Think about those in your life whom you love and cherish. How do you show your love to them? You make sure they get the bigger steak, the last of the salad dressing, the best seat to watch TV. Maybe you relinquish the TV remote to your spouse, or you make pancakes in the shape of reindeer for your kids or grandkids — the list is endless.

If you were paying attention during our review of the flight attendant's announcement, you'd realize that depriving yourself of the basic luxury of *love* will not win you a medal of honor. You were never meant to live a life of deprivation, especially when it comes to love.

> *Change your mentality from perfection to progress.*

Just so we're crystal clear, let me reiterate this simple fact: self-deprivation is the exact opposite of love. Anything worth doing takes time. Give yourself the time you need to develop a healthy and balanced respect toward yourself.

Life is not a sprint. It's a marathon. Plan accordingly.

Again, this is not about perfection.

This journey is all about *progress.*

Determine to take one small step of progress every single day. Stop living in the all-or-nothing mentality that will trap you every single time if you aim for perfection. Love takes time to nurture and grow. It's a principle, no matter to whom you apply it.

Change your mentality from "perfection" to "progress." Progress moves forward. Perfection will forever keep you stuck and frustrated, never moving forward. If you're stuck in procrastination, then you are no stranger to being consistently stuck.

The quest for perfection will kill dreams, creativity, and personal growth every single time. Striving only for progress, on the other hand, has benefits. It leads to dreaming big, to enhanced creativity, to achieving personal growth, and to realizing optimal health.

Here's perhaps the most freeing thing you will ever hear about procrastination. You'll want to underline, star, highlight, and put a big note on this one. It's a real myth buster!

Procrastination is a combination of perfectionism and the fear of failure. Neither is healthy, neither helps you move forward, neither gives you breathing room in your life. They have the opposite effect.

Remember, your present situation is not your destination. You have the power to change direction at any given time during your journey. Change your mind and your body will follow.

For inspiration, consider these words:

> *Blessed be the God and Father of our Lord Jesus Christ, who has blessed us in Christ with every spiritual blessing in the heavenly places, even as he chose us in him before the foundation of the world, that we should be holy and blameless before him. In love he predestined us for adoption to himself as sons through Jesus Christ, according to the purpose of his will, to the praise of his glorious grace, with which he has blessed us in the Beloved. In him we have redemption through his blood, the forgiveness of our trespasses, according to the riches of his grace, which he lavished upon us, in all wisdom and insight.*
> (Ephesians 1:3–8, ESV)

God saw fit to lavish His love upon us while we were yet sinners and separated from Him. If God loves us enough to give His Son for us as ransom, do you not think it's time you fully walk in the love He has given you? That includes loving and forgiving yourself.

God will never ask for perfection from you. He provided it through grace and faith in His only Son. God will, however, daily give you the strength as you move toward progress when you invite Him into your circumstances.

WALKING IN GRACE

W hat is grace?
"Grace," is defined as:

> *When used as a noun: is favor or goodwill, a manifestation of favor, especially by a superior.*
>
> *When used as a verb/object: to lend or add grace to or to favor or honor.*
>
> *Synonyms for grace are agility, beauty, dignity, ease, elegance, finesse, poise, refinement, balance, etiquette, gracefulness.* (Dictionary.com)

Those are all wonderful and descriptive ways to look at grace, but I want to focus on what God says grace is, according to His Word.

Let's start with Ephesians 2:8–9, ESV: "For by grace you have been saved through faith. And this is not your own doing; it is the gift of God, not a result of works, so that no one may boast."

Grace is *not getting what you deserve.* Have you ever been in a situation where you did something wrong and, instead of receiving punishment, you were given another chance? Has it ever gone the other way? Have you ever received a punishment that fit the crime?

For example: Let's say you were in New York, and you got pulled over by a police officer for speeding. The fine on a first conviction can range from $90 to $600. That penalty is based on a set of predetermined rules and regulations. If you were driving less than 10 miles per hour over the limit, your ticket would cost from $90 to $150. If you were speeding between 11 and 30 mph over the limit, it would cost you between $90 and $300.

Now, let's say you were speeding more than 31 mph over the limit; the fine for that is between $360 and $600. The fines also increase depending on whether this were your second or third conviction.

And don't forget about the moving violation surcharges, driver assessment fees, other fees, and driver's license points that will accumulate on top of the speeding ticket. These fines and penalties vary throughout the United States, according to the state in which they occur.

What if someone were to pay those penalties on your behalf? What if that person never had committed that crime but loved you enough to pay whatever the penalty demanded?

> *Grace changes the course of history.*

In Romans 6:23, ESV, the Bible shows us, "For the wages of sin is death, but the free gift of God is eternal life in Christ Jesus our Lord."

We all deserve death because we have all sinned. Grace is mercy that looks at you and says, "I love you, and I want to extend grace to you in your current situation. I will gladly fulfill the Law so you can become righteous through My sacrifice."

Is grace extended for everyone?

Yes, everyone can receive grace. Grace changes the course of history. Grace changes the trajectory of where each one of us was headed. Grace took our place on that cross. Jesus lived without sin. He was the perfect lamb. He was the sacrifice for you and me. He gave His life so that you and I could experience grace, love, mercy, and most of all, live and walk in a relationship with God the Father that was restored because Jesus went to the cross and literally took our place.

2 Corinthians 5:21, ESV, declares, "For our sake He made Him to be sin who knew no sin, so that in Him we might become the righteousness of God."

If you have been held captive by the death grip of addiction over your heart and life, just ask God for His help. This is when you must extend grace to yourself as you are sorting out your long and sometimes tumultuous relationship with food. I encourage you to give yourself the gift of grace when it comes to food and your journey toward healing. The Bible is quite clear about serving two masters — you simply cannot.

No one can serve two masters, for either he will hate the one and love the other, or he will be devoted to the one and despise the other. You cannot serve God and money. (Matthew 6:24, ESV)

This reference is talking specifically about the difference between God and money. I believe this biblical principle can and should be applied to any area of your life. For the purpose of this book, I'm comparing God and your relationship with food.

You can serve and love God with all your heart and still not walk in peace with food. Food is vital to sustaining you physically. Somewhere along the way, it has become more than it was ever intended to be. It has taken the place of comfort, joy, and fulfillment, meaning it temporarily calms our fears and, for some, becomes a very dear and faithful friend.

Should we enjoy the food we eat? Yes, it should be enjoyable, and we should be enjoying the company of others while we eat. However, if it has become an idol in your life, or an event done in private, I ask you to examine your relationship with food.

What exactly are you getting out of this relationship? Are you fulfilled? Are you free? Are you eating when you're not truly hungry?

If you answered yes to the last question, then what is at the root of the compulsion to eat?

For me, it was for comfort, even if only temporary. I also used food as if to magically give myself the strength to face something hard.

You can't truly walk in grace around food if you are serving two masters. I challenge you to see your relationship with food for what it really is. Whatever the conclusion, there is a solution.

The solution, I believe, is to bring this area of your life under the authority and grace of God. When you submit it to God, you are bringing your darkest, deepest, most ugly secret out into the open where you can rely on Him to bring light and healing.

Yes, I hear you. You say, "But I've already done that a thousand times before."

I commend you on taking that step. What you need to know next is that it is only the first part of the solution. Giving this part of your darkest secret to God is an amazing first step. It takes courage to really look deep into your heart and your life to see you can't control this situation.

The next step I'm asking you to take is to walk in grace and then adjust as necessary.

I'd like to remind you that when you've been engaging in a certain pattern or behavior for an extended period, it will take time and patience to change. Start with small steps. They will add up quickly.

I have a simple quiz you can use the next time you reach for food. Use my ABC test:

A: ASK YOURSELF IF YOU ARE REACHING FOR FOOD OUT OF PHYSICAL HUNGER.

If yes, eat.
If no, keep reading the ABCs.

B: BE AWARE OF TRIGGERS.

If you are not eating out of physical hunger, then what triggered you to reach for food? There could be an endless number of things that trigger you.

Remember how I shared the fact that conflict used to be a trigger for me? Again, it was not conflict itself but rather the meaning I attached to it that drove me to eat when I was faced with the potential for it.

What triggered you? It could be conflict, anger, finances, an impromptu meeting with your boss, judgment from others, boredom, disappointment. The list is endless, but it will hold important clues for you.

C: CONSIDER THE DEEPER MEANING YOU'VE ASSIGNED TO THESE TRIGGERS.

These could be the very things that will lead to your breakthrough.

D: DEVOTE TIME TO PRAY ABOUT THESE TRIGGERS.

Be sure to schedule part of your time in prayer every day to ask the Spirit of God how to overcome these long-held beliefs that have become patterns.

E: EXPECT HELP FROM THE LORD.

Let me encourage you with these powerful Scriptures:

> *Finally, be strong in the Lord and in the strength of His might.* (Ephesians 6:10, ESV)

> *A tranquil heart gives life to the flesh, but envy makes the bones rot.* (Proverbs 14:30, ESV)

> *When a man's folly brings his way to ruin, his heart rages against the Lord.* (Proverbs 19:3, ESV)

> *Great peace have those who love your law; nothing can make them stumble.* (Psalm 119:165, ESV)

My personal favorite in time of need:

> *Do not be anxious about anything, but in everything by prayer and supplication with thanksgiving let your request be made known to God. And the peace of God, which surpasses all understanding, will guard your hearts and your minds in Christ Jesus.* (Philippians 4:6–7, ESV)

RESOURCES: FILL UP ON SCRIPTURES

For the grace of God has appeared, bringing salvation for all people, training us to renounce ungodliness and worldly passions, and to live self-controlled, upright, and godly lives in the present age, waiting for our blessed hope, the appearing of the glory of our great God and Savior Jesus Christ. (Titus 2:11–13, ESV)

And everyone who thus hopes in Him purifies himself as He is pure. (1 John 3:3, ESV)

Do not be anxious or worried about anything, but in everything [every circumstance and situation] by prayer and petition with thanksgiving, continue to make your [specific] requests known to God. And the peace of God [that peace which reassures the heart, that peace] which transcends all understanding, [that peace which] stands guard over your hearts and your minds in Christ Jesus [is yours]. (Philippians 4:6–7, Amplified Bible [AMP])

We know that our old self was crucified with him in order that the body of sin might be brought to nothing, so that we would no longer be enslaved to sin. (Romans 6:6, ESV)

But you are a chosen race, a royal priesthood, a holy nation, a people for his own possession, that you may proclaim the excellencies of him who called you out of darkness into his marvelous light. (1 Peter 2:9, ESV)

Therefore, if anyone is in Christ, he is a new creation. The old has passed away; behold, the new has come. (2 Corinthians 5:17, ESV)

A love letter from God. Let His Word dwell richly in you.

> *But to all who did receive him, who believed in his name, he gave the right to become children of God.* (John 1:12, ESV)

If you have never prayed and asked Jesus to come into your heart, please consider these Scriptures and pray to receive Jesus as your personal Lord and Savior.

> *We are all sinners* (Romans 3:23, ESV): *"For all have sinned and fall short of the glory of God."*

> *We receive eternal life as a free gift* (Romans 6:23, ESV): *"For the wages of sin is death, but the free gift of God is eternal life in Christ Jesus."*

> *God demonstrated His love for us* (Romans 5:8, ESV): *"But God shows His love for us in that while we were still sinners, Christ dies for us."*

> *We must trust and surrender to Jesus as Lord* (Romans 10:9–10, ESV): *"Because, if you confess with your mouth that Jesus is Lord and believe in your heart that God raised Him from the dead, you will be saved. For with the heart, one believes and is justified, and with the mouth one confesses and is saved."*

> *This is our assurance of salvation through Jesus* (Romans 10:13, ESV): *"For everyone who calls on the name of the Lord will be saved."*

If you have already believed in your heart and confessed with your mouth that Jesus is your Lord, but you are not living for Him, please know that you can come right back into a right relationship with Him again by simply asking Him. There is nothing that can separate you from the love of God.

> *For I am sure that neither death nor life, nor angels nor rulers, nor things present nor things to come, nor powers, nor height nor depth, nor anything else in all creation, will be able to separate us from the love of God in Christ Jesus our Lord.* (Romans 8:38–39, ESV)

CONCLUSION

We have walked through the three main areas that make up our lives.

First, we focused on the mind by taking a truthful evaluation, finding your moment of truth, discussing why diets don't work, and exposing why it's not your fault that you've not been able to keep the weight off.

Then we discussed the importance of taking every thought captive.

Next, we looked at the area of the soul. Here, we talked about ownership, feeding your soul, how emotions are a gift from God, and how following the Spirit of God brings life and peace.

Then we moved to discussing the body. We examined how vital it is to get proper sleep so your body can heal and process food and emotions correctly, how important hydration is for overall health, what real nourishment to the body is, and, finally, how movement doesn't have to be a four-letter word.

I hope you took the time with each step to work through the exercises, absorb the information, and take advantage of the resources listed at the end of each section to make this part of your journey personal. That is where the real power is.

The things you do day in and day out become habits and routines.

Information is great. However, information in itself is not going to lead you to transformation. Transformation is what we all long for and earnestly seek.

Alexander Graham Bell was correct when he said, "The difference between success and failure is the ability to take action." (history.com/ topics/inventions/alexander-graham-bell)

Information can get you started, but for transformation or change to occur, you must act.

Remember, past attempts and efforts don't define you. The fact that you have tried so many things so many times to find the answers to achieving freedom with food is a testament to your determination and to your intuitive knowledge that something deep needs to be addressed.

It also tells me that you have been listening to your heart. Your heart will know when you've found peace and when you've found the correct series of adjustments that will bring freedom around food.

Most likely, the reason you couldn't break free and find peace before is that you hadn't yet discovered the root of your issue around food. Food is not the problem; thus, food is not the solution. You need to get to the root of the issue to experience real freedom.

You can temporarily change your behavior by going on a diet for a few weeks. Will you lose some weight? Probably. The problem is, it's never a lasting change and it seldom brings true health. The weight loss is not sustainable for long-term success.

I hope and pray that as you made your way through the steps outlined in this book, you made *heart* changes. That's where the transformation happens. It happens from the inside out. Not the other way around.

When a series of small changes start to happen, they usher in transformation. Everyone is looking for that moment of "fireworks," or for that final piece of information, the key for the padlock that has kept you bound. The truth is that transformation happens little by little.

Do you want to know the biggest and best-kept secret about transformation? One success builds on another. Those small, seemingly insignificant changes are what make the entire foundation upon which habits can change. You have to build a foundation as you go. That is the starting point. The secret is out!

The foundation and momentum for more lasting change are built one choice at a time.

The bottom line is that you can take ownership of your health no matter what state it is in right now. God is willing and ready to help you as you take the steps necessary to reclaim your health.

I've heard it said that when you are interested, you do what's convenient. When you are committed, you do what it takes.

Let me ask you, are you interested or are you committed?

Don't get healthy for your friend, spouse, grandmother, or anyone else. Get healthy for yourself. You are the only one who can make a change.

The sooner you start taking these small steps toward health, hope, and healing, the sooner you will reap the benefits. Start today. Don't allow the devil of procrastination, perfection, and the all-or-nothing mentality rob you of true and lasting health, hope, and healing.

You deserve to live in a healthy body to glorify God with your body today. Your identity is in Christ. You are an overcomer, a world-changer, and deeply loved.

ACKNOWLEDGEMENTS

I have wanted to write a book for as long as I can remember.

Saturday mornings were reserved for a trip to our local library, and I loaded up every single week. In addition, my mother always made sure there was an ample supply of good, educational, and fun books in our home.

Some of my favorite memories from childhood were monthly family outings to the Glendale Center — now called Glendale Mall — where we would visit the biggest bookstore in our area. Logos Bookstore was huge, and I looked forward to it every single time.

Those outings were always a source of great joy. I marked them on my calendar. My siblings and I could use our allowance from chores and odd jobs, or a recent windfall of birthday money, to purchase any book of our choice. I remember running to the mystery section on multiple occasions to look for the very next book in the Nancy Drew or Hardy Boys series, the newest Judy Blume book, or even the latest novel to receive the coveted Newbery Medal.

I loved words and could get lost in books for hours at a time. I think what I liked best about books is how they can shape our world and open new possibilities with the simple turn of a page. I have always held books, education, and learning in high esteem. I value words and know they can reach the recesses of our hearts in ways that are astounding.

First, I want to acknowledge my mother, Anna Lindener, who has always been my biggest cheerleader. She encouraged and challenged me to always keep striving to be my best, regardless of the task at hand.

In particular, I owe her a debt of gratitude for having the foresight to sign me up for the entrance exam for Culver Girls Academy (CGA) in the summer of 1980. I was nervous about the exam, but I was accepted. I was able to attend Culver Girls Academy the final three years of high school on scholarship. I have a deep appreciation for how CGA helped change the trajectory of my life by providing me with incredible opportunities. I also developed life-long friends there who are still a source of joy for me to this day.

Many people have had a tremendous influence on my life over the years.

To all the teachers who saw something in me long before I did, thank you for believing in me and encouraging me to pursue my passion.

My family was an incredible source of strength and comfort for me as I embarked upon the journey to complete this book. My husband pitched in, cooked meals, and took care of the dogs while I was in my office, typing away.

To my daughter, thank you for your kind words and encouragement.

To my son, thank you for being such an independent young man.

My extended family and friends have been a huge support during this journey.

I also want to thank those who helped with the book launch and who read this book as part of the review process.

I would especially like to thank you, dear reader, for reading *Beyond the Scale*. I hope it becomes a pivotal point in your journey to take back your own health. Use the tools and steps provided in this book to bring you closer to realizing your dreams and goals.

Finally, to my Heavenly Father, thank you for your faithfulness.

ABOUT THE AUTHOR

Debra has always had a passion for helping others and for making their lives better. She first attended nursing school, thinking it was the path she would take, but she ultimately followed her heart and found her passion. This led her to health coaching.

Debra went back to school to become a Certified International Health Coach. She now knows that health encompasses so much more than what you eat or drink. Her approach incorporates a holistic method that helps her clients take back their health to find freedom, joy, and happiness. True health encompasses mind, spirit, and body. Each aspect is crucial and needs to be addressed to bring lasting health, hope, and healing to your life.

She is grateful to have had the pleasure of fulfilling her heart's biggest desire of becoming a mother and helping to raise the next generation to love God with all their mind, soul, and heart.

Debra resides in North Carolina with her family. She still enjoys reading, sewing, swimming, music, and writing. She has two adorable Cavachon dogs, Apollo and Gemini.

Debra struggled for years with emotional eating, self-worth issues, and self-sabotage. When she addressed the root of the issue, she began to experience freedom in every area of her life.

Drawing on her own experience, training, and expertise, she takes clients step by step so they can break free from the grip of addiction and live the life God has designed for them to live.

Her programs have successfully helped others take back their health and start enjoying their lives again. As a weight-loss coach, Bible teacher, speaker, supportive mentor, and wellness authority, she helps women obtain optimal health and reach their health goals using diet and exercise tools and behavioral psychology principles. She has coached women to successfully shed their weight, as well as the shame and regret that often accompany it.

Take advantage of an amazing <u>free discovery call</u> or go to https:// schedulewithdebramoss.as.me, where Debra will talk through your health challenges and discover a path to get you unstuck.

CONNECT WITH DEBRA:

https://www.debramosshealthcoach.com/
debramosshealthcoach@outlook.com
https://www.facebook.com/debramossintegrativenutritionhealthcoach
https://www.instagram.com/debramosshealthcoach/
https://www.linkedin.com/in/debra-moss-4b286b231/

Don't forget to use all the great bonus items Debra provided throughout the book to help you gain momentum for your health journey.

Download them from https://www.debramosshealthcoach.com/bonuses.